THE ILLUSTRATED
WORLD OF TOLKIEN

To Lucy Pessell and Sarah Vaughan

An Hachette UK Company
www.hachette.co.uk

First published in Great Britain in 2019 by Cassell,
an imprint of Octopus Publishing Group Ltd
Carmelite House, 50 Victoria Embankment, London EC4Y 0DZ
www.octopusbooks.co.uk

ISBN 978-0-7537-3380-6

A CIP catalogue record for this book is available from the British Library

Printed and bound in China

10 9 8 7 6 5 4 3 2 1

Publisher: Lucy Pessell
Designer: Hannah Coughlin
Editor: Sarah Vaughan
Senior Production Manager: Peter Hunt

Illustrations by Victor Ambrus, Graham Bence, John Blanche, Jaroslav
Bradac, Allan Curless, Sally Davies, Jon Davis, Michael Foreman, Linda
Garland, Melvyn Grant, Sam Hadley, David Kearney, Pauline Martin, Mauro
Mazzara, Ian Miller, Andrew Mockett, Turner Mohan, Andrea Piparo, Sue
Porter, Lidia Postma, Kip Rasmussen, David Roberts, Šárka Škorpíková,
Jamie Whyte

THE ILLUSTRATED WORLD OF TOLKIEN

DAVID DAY

CASSELL ILLUSTRATED

BILBO BAGGINS
LIDIA POSTMA

CONTENTS:

GANDALF
LIDIA POSTMA

AN INTRODUCTION DAVID DAY

The Illustrated World of Tolkien is a gallery of some of the finest Tolkien-inspired art from a unique and exclusive picture library that has been created over the last 40 years. It began with the 1979 publication of *A Tolkien Bestiary*: the first fully illustrated reader's guide to Middle-earth and the Undying Lands. *A Tolkien Bestiary* appeared just two years after the posthumous publication of J R R Tolkien's *The Silmarillion*: a book that for the first time gave readers of *The Hobbit* and *The Lord of the Rings* some indication of the immense scope of Tolkien's mythology and cosmology.

In 1992, *A Tolkien Bestiary* was updated and expanded with new illustrators in the more comprehensive *Tolkien: the Illustrated Encyclopaedia*. Then again, in 2002, another gathering of artists resulted in the creation of *The World of Tolkien: Mythological Sources of Lord of the Rings*.

In 2013, the decision was made to begin what became a comprehensive, yet compact, six-volume reference library on J.R.R Tolkien's Middle-earth and the Undying Lands in a uniformly designed series of handsome flexi-bound books. In this exciting new format, beyond providing comprehensive texts, the library is gorgeously illustrated by a combination of established artists and fresh new talents, packaged in attractive and collectible editions.

The Illustrated World of Tolkien is curated from all of these nine books. And here, with the large format provided by *The Illustrated World of Tolkien*, we can not only celebrate some of the finest Tolkien-inspired art gathered over the past 40 years, but also provide the opportunity to celebrate the artists themselves. And indeed, give voice to the artists themselves by providing them with this avenue to share their own stories, sources of inspiration, and reveal something of their lives.

With *The Illustrated World of Tolkien*, you won't need to be an expert in Elvish to find your way around Middle-earth and the Undying Lands. It has been written and organized in a way that is both informative and accessible to the general reader. The book is mostly written for those who have read at least one of the books – or have seen the movies and wish to read the books. It is also, of course, for those who know Tolkien well, and just wish to immerse themselves in art that celebrates Tolkien's world.

Quite by serendipity, this reference library series strongly resembles another collectible series of beautiful, illustrated books that inspired Tolkien's childhood fascination with fairy tales and myths. This was Andrew Lang's famous *Fairy Book* series (1889-1910) that introduced the young Tolkien to "the nameless North of Sigurd of the Völsungs, and the prince of all dragons." Like Andrew Lang's famous multi-volume *Fairy Books of Many Colours*, each of our collectible, illustrated reference library books is distinguished by a different colour.

It has been one of the great pleasures of my life that in the making of many beautiful books, I have collaborated with so many wonderful artists. This is certainly true with this book. However, the broad range of my writing extends from fantasy and mythology, to poetry and children's literature, to history, ecology and natural history. And in each, I have worked with and been published with many of the remarkable artists and illustrators. From the extraordinary and outrageous like Ralph Steadman and Gerald Scarfe, to living legends like impressionist Feliks Topolski and the great wildlife artist, Maurice Wilson. And beyond the array of artists in this Tolkien reference collection, I also number as friends and colleagues two of the most celebrated Tolkien illustrators: Alan Lee and John Howe. Alan Lee and I have produced two beautiful books: *Castles* in 1984 and *Tolkien's Ring* in 1994. With John Howe, I toured the castles of the Rhine in the making of the documentary *Looking for the Hobbit – The Lost God of the Rhine* in 2014.

For the purposes of *The Illustrated World of Tolkien*, we decided to produce a book of illustrations unique to this series, and independent of the images appearing in the popular media of films and motion pictures. In this book, I am pleased to be able to reveal a treasure trove of illustrations of Tolkien's world that has grown and gathered over the last four decades. The aim is to reveal something of the imaginative sweep and splendour of Tolkien's epic world. But it is also to involve the reader to discover something of the artist's experience, inspiration and vision in the creation of these works of art.

In *The Illustrated World of Tolkien* we celebrate both the art and the artist.

THE GREY HAVENS
MICHAEL FOREMAN

PERMISSION KIP RASMUSSEN

I am a family therapist by trade and have spent most of my career trying to help people and their families with all kinds of emotional struggles. But, like millions of others, I turn to the works of Tolkien to recharge. I love *The Lord of the Rings* and *The Hobbit* but, for me *The Silmarillion* ranks as one of the pre-eminent works of art ever created. I was so struck by it that I craved seeing the images in paint. At first, I was very hesitant because I wasn't an experienced painter but still wanted to do justice to the mighty work. Then I found some encouragement in the words of the great man himself:

> "The cycles should be linked to a majestic whole, and yet leave scope for other minds and hands wielding paint and music and drama."
> —J R R Tolkien, Letter 131 to Milton Waldman (1951)

So there it was: permission to paint his work. That was enough for me. I'll paint it to my life's end.

DO NOT LAUGH J R R TOLKIEN

"Do not laugh! But once upon a time (my crest has long since fallen) I had a mind to make a body of more or less connected legend, ranging from the large and cosmogonic, to the level of romantic fairy-story – the larger founded on the lesser in contact with the earth, the lesser drawing splendour from the vast backcloths – which I could dedicate simply to: to England; to my country. It should possess the tone and quality that I desired, somewhat cool and clear, be redolent of our 'air' (the clime and soil of the North West, meaning Britain and the hither parts of Europe: not Italy or the Aegean, still less the East), and, while possessing (if I could achieve it) the fair elusive beauty that some call Celtic (though it is rarely found in genuine ancient Celtic things), it should be 'high', purged of the gross, and fit for the more adult mind of a land long now steeped in poetry. I would draw some of the great tales in fullness, and leave many only placed in the scheme, and sketched. The cycles should be linked to a majestic whole, and yet leave scope for other minds and hands, wielding paint and music and drama. Absurd."

TUOR AND VORONWË SEEK GONDOLIN
KIP RASMUSSEN

IN THE BEGINNING

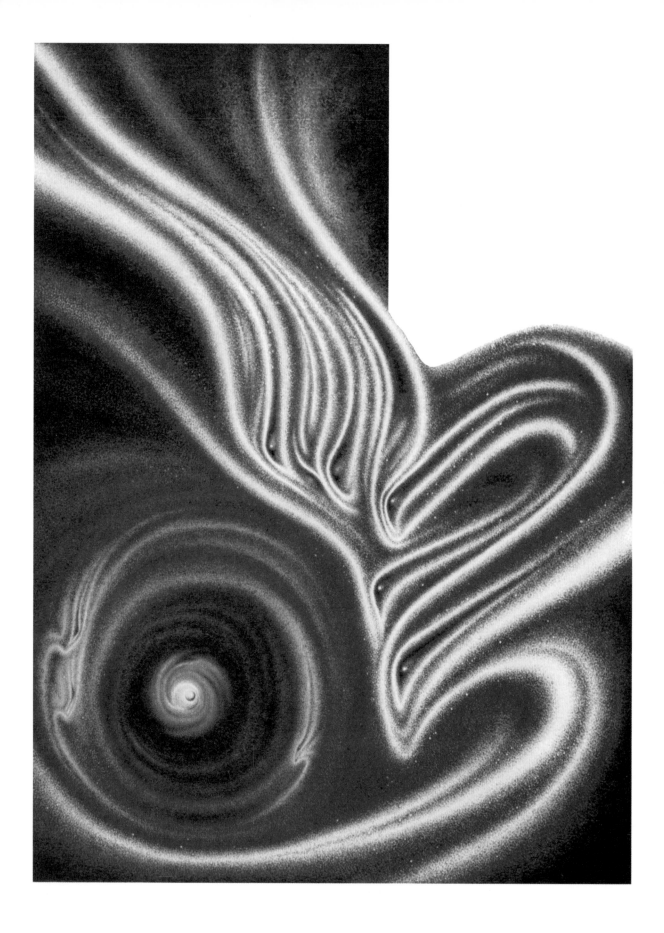

ERU CREATES THE AINUR
MAURO MAZZARA

THE CREATION OF ARDA

The creator-god of Tolkien's world of Arda, was Eru "The One", known to the Elves as Ilúvatar ("Allfather"). Arda is the High Elven (Quenya) name for Tolkien's fictional world, encompassing the mortal lands of Middle-earth and the immortal Undying Lands of Aman. Arda, Tolkien insisted, is not another planet, but our world: the planet Earth. As the author himself explained: "The theatre of my tale is this earth, the one in which we now live, but the historical period is imaginary." The connection is made clear in the name: Arda is connected to the Old High German Erda and Gothic airþa, both of which translate as "Earth".

Eru was in part inspired by the Judeo-Christian creator-god, Yahweh/Jehovah, although there are important differences in conception.

In the beginning, Tolkien tells us that in his cosmogony (creation myth), Eru's "thoughts" took the form of entities known as the Ainur, or "Holy Ones", vastly powerful spirits that are comparable to the Judeo-Christian angels and archangels.

Eru commands the Ainur to sing in a celestial choir, thereby revealing his vision of "what was, and is, and is to come." Eru creates and wakens first the Elves and then Men (just as Yahweh/Jehovah creates Adam). Like the God of the Bible, Eru is conceived of as making decisive interventions in world history, such as the destruction of the fleet of King Ar-Pharazôn and the re-embodiment of Gandalf after his death in Moria.

In most other respects, however, the early Judeo-Christian world is very unlike Tolkien's world. Tolkien purposely created a world that is without formal religion, and Eru is far from being the vengeful, jealous deity of the Old Testament (it is Melkor/Morgoth who perhaps takes on these aspects).

THE ART OF CREATION   DAVID DAY

In 1979, the British artist Pauline Martin created this calming, lyrically beautiful watercolour of the Vision of Creation "like a globed light in the Void". Some thirty-seven years later, the Italian artist Mauro Mazzara imagines a titanic Eru Ilúvatar as the Creator commanding all the elemental forces of the universe in his spectacular interpretation of the Music of the Ainur. In these two stunning and stylistically distinct visions of the Creation of Arda, no better perspective can be gained on how the art of illustrating Tolkien's cosmos has evolved over the last four decades.

THE CREATION OF ARDA
PAULINE MARTIN

THE AINUR

As Tolkien informs us, the Ainur, many of whom subsequently enter the created world of Arda, are "beings of the same order of beauty, power and majesty as the gods of higher mythology." Indeed, those Ainur who enter Arda become known as the Valar and the Maiar, taking physical forms comparable to the gods of ancient Greek, Roman and Germanic mythology. And although the inhabitants of Tolkien's world do not quite worship these "gods", the beliefs they hold surrounding these angelic powers are much closer to those of the ancient Greeks, Romans and Germanic peoples than they are to the fierce monotheism of the ancient Israelites.

THE VALAR

The Valar were the fourteen ruling Powers of Arda, angelic beings who, after the creation of Arda, enter into its "circles" and shape various aspects of it. Many of the Valar are associated with a particular realm, such as the sea, starry night sky, rocks and mountains and plants and animals. Most form male-and-female pairs ("spouses") and a few are siblings. Except in Tolkien's earliest writings, they do not have offspring.

Tolkien did not conceive of his Valar as gods, even if they sometimes seem to be perceived as such by Elves, Men and others. They are not worshipped (even if they are revered or called upon), and there are few mythological stories attached to their names. They are above all manifestations of good creative power, nurturing order and stability in a world that is constantly threatened by the evil powers of disorder and chaos, manifested in Morgoth and Sauron.

Nonetheless, in creating his "pantheon", Tolkien was clearly influenced by both the Greco-Roman gods (and occasionally heroes) and Norse gods.

THE LAMPS OF THE VALAR   DAVID DAY

Šárka Škorpíková's idyllic watercolour of the Isle of Almaren, in the midst of a great lake in Middle-earth, was the first dwelling-place of the Valar. Šárka provides a utopian vision of the Spring of Arda: a peaceful pastoral age when the world was illuminated by the sacred light of Illuin, one of two sacred Lamps of the Valar. This vision is in stark contrast to Linda Garland's nightmarish scene portraying the toppled ruin of Ormal, the second of the two titanic Lamps of the Valar in *The Destruction of the Lamps*. Both Lamps were cast down and extinguished by the mighty rebel Vala, Melkor, and the world was rocked and broken open by a mighty tumult that followed. Almaren was utterly destroyed and Middle-earth was plunged into darkness and chaos that lasted for many ages.

THE DESTRUCTION OF THE LAMPS
LINDA GARLAND

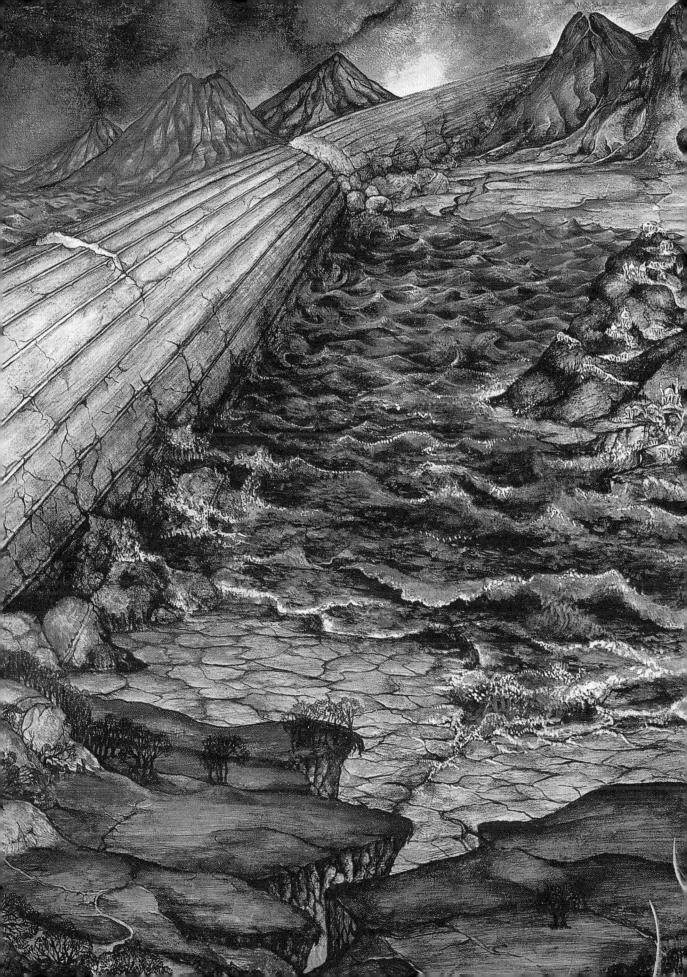

AULË AND YAVANNA
JAROSLAV BRADAC

⊶————⊷

AULË AND YAVANNA

In Tolkien's Valarian god Aulë the Smith, the Maker of Mountains, we have the counterpart of the Greek god Hephaestus (the Roman Vulcan). Both are capable of forging untold wonders from the metals and elements of the Earth. Both are smiths, armourers and jewellers. Like Hephaestus, Aulë is depicted as a true craftsman and artisan, someone who creates for the joy of making, not for the sake of possession or gaining power and dominion over others.

Aulë is also the maker of Tolkien's race of Dwarves. These in their origins are very like the race of automatons created by Hephaestus, who appeared to be living creatures, but in fact were machines similar to robots designed to help in the smithy with the beating of metal and the working of the forges. In Tolkien, Aulë creates the Dwarves because he is impatient for pupils who can carry out his knowledge and craft. However, they are given true life and independent minds only at the command of Eru Ilúvatar. Among the Norsemen, Aulë's counterpart as the smith to the gods and heroes is Völundr. Among the Anglo-Saxons, he is Wayland.

In Tolkien's legendarium, Yavanna is the Valarian queen of the Earth (Kementári) who watches over all living things. In the form of a woman, she is described as tall and clothed in green, though "Some there are who have seen her standing like a tree under heaven, crowned with the Sun; and from all its branches there spilled a golden dew upon the barren earth." Her younger sister is Vána, the Ever Young, who brings forth blossoming flowers, and she is the spouse of Aulë.

Yavanna has a direct parallel in the Greco-Roman pantheon, in the earth-mother goddess Demeter/Ceres. In Demeter's grief for her daughter Persephone (who bears some resemblance to Vána), which causes nature to go into hibernation, there is a parallel with the Sleep of Yavanna. After the destruction of the Two Lamps, the queen of the Earth walks "in the shadow of Middle-earth, grieving because the growth and promise of the Spring of Arda was stayed" and causes the animals and plants to go into a slumber that lasts many years.

IMAGINING THE "GODS" DAVID DAY

In *A Tolkien Bestiary*, it was decided that each of the major races or humanoid groupings were to be given a distinctive artist throughout the book. The challenging task of creating convincing images of the angelic spirits of Tolkien's Ainur, Valar and Maiar was assigned to Jaroslav Bradac, a talented Czech artist who previously created a remarkable artist's portrayal and film of Hermann Hesse's *Steppenwolf*. His Ainur were revealed as archetypal elemental powers and his Valar were akin to the ancient pagan Greco-Roman gods; while his Maiar convincingly resembled demigods and nature spirits.

THE POWER OF NARRATIVE FICTION
KIP RASMUSSEN

Among the great miracles of existence is the power of narrative fiction. Like music, humour, poetry and the other creative arts, the acts of fiction transform the lives of both the creators and those who partake of the art. Why should we care so much about characters, lands and events which have never existed? I don't have the definitive answer to this question, but I do know that the work of Tolkien has struck at a level in my life that is both elemental and expansive.

As an illustrator, it is impossible to recount all the myriad inspiring elements of Tolkien's work. Reading *The Hobbit* and *The Lord of the Rings* was riveting. There were so many wonderful aspects to fire the spirit, from the bucolic Hobbiton to the mountainous redoubt of Rivendell to the malevolent forest of Mirkwood to the great city of Minas Tirith. Smaug and Bard, Aragorn and Arwen, Éowyn and the Witch-king; there is so much to imagine and illustrate.

But if these books were riveting, for me, *The Silmarillion* was life altering. Everything we love about *The Hobbit* and *The Lord of the Rings* is there, but in greater measure: more gods, Dragons, Balrogs, Elves, warriors, Orcs, Ents, Dwarves and lords of destruction. Sauron is only a servant of the first dark lord. And the wars; conflicts so massive that the Battle of the Pelennor Fields might not have been counted among the First Age battles worth numbering. And we should not forget the origin stories. When we wonder where something in *The Lord of the Rings* originated, we find that Tolkien wrote a marvelous story which answers this question. Who would write a tale in which two married gods dispute the mastery of trees resulting in the origin story of the Ents? It is almost beyond belief that many ardent Tolkien fans justifiably count Tolkien as a genius but have not read what I consider to be his greatest work. It is one of my fondest wishes to help fans of Tolkien to experience *The Silmarillion*. This is why I paint.

DIVINE SPIRITS   DAVID DAY

Although Jaroslav Bradac's Valar were definitive portrayals of the powers of Arda throughout the pages of *A Tolkien Bestiary*, they did not by any means remain as uncontested interpretations of these entities. One need only look at Kip Rasmussen's evocative and idyllic *Aulë and Yavanna Look Over Their Creations* to see a very different but entirely convincing portrayal of these divine archetypal spirits of the mountains and forests of Arda, or, taking another tact, Mauro Mazzara's volcanic portrait of Aulë the Maker of Mountains to recognize how much Tolkien was inspired by the Greco-Roman smith god Vulcan-Hephaestus.

AULË, MAKER OF MOUNTAINS
MAURO MAZZARA

A CHALLENGE   MAURO MAZZARA

Since I was a kid I have been influenced by the amazing fantasy movies of that time: *Willow*, *The Neverending Story*, and so on. As a teenager I finally discovered fantasy literature. Luckily there weren't smartphones then, so I grew up a very hungry reader.

One day I was told about this epic and very heavy (literally) book called *The Lord of the Rings*. More than 1200 pages! I took it as a personal challenge at first. I remember some difficulties in reading all those names and genealogies. (I'm a very visual person: I need to create images in my head and I have attention issues when it comes to numbers and names.) But then the journey started. And I really wished I could have stayed in it forever. After that I read *The Hobbit* – a lovely adventure, deeper than it seemed at first.

I had the luck to enjoy Tolkien books before the movies were released. I remember the excitement in 2001, when I went to watch *The Fellowship of the Ring* with my friends. I felt comfortable watching the movies, even if I didn't like some of the changes from the book, because the world had been created on the works of John Howe and Alan Lee, two illustrators I've always venerated. Years later I had the privilege and honour to be published among them in a magazine. Sometimes dreams come true.

"I feel thin, sort of stretched, like butter scraped over too much bread", Bilbo says to Frodo. I've used this quote in a song I recently wrote for my band "Oniromantic". This might give you a sense of how much Tolkien's words are still in my mind, even today.

When it comes to my illustrations, I always search for Tolkien's descriptions of what I have to illustrate. I enjoy illustrating scenes or characters not present in movies or in too many other illustrations much more, because I can approach them using just my imagination, without any kind of visual memory.

KINGDOM OF THE VALAR
DAVID DAY

Michael Foreman was among the first artists commissioned for *A Tolkien Bestiary* and was believed to be the perfect illustrator for Valimar, the City of the Holy Ones. Michael had already illustrated 40 books, and would go on to publish over 200 more, twice winning the prestigious Kate Greenaway Medal. It was his particular challenge to portray Laurelin the Golden and Telperion the White: the sacred Trees of the Valar that shone eternally with brilliant gold and silver light during the ages of bliss and contentment in the Undying Lands.

TREES OF THE VALAR
MICHAEL FOREMAN

SOMETHING DIFFERENT
MICHAEL FOREMAN

I have always enjoyed doing a wide range of work, fact and fiction, for both children and adults.

When I got the chance to make images for Tolkien, I was thrilled. At around this time, in addition to writing my own stories, I was working on *Anthologies of Stories* by the Brothers Grimm, *Hans Christian Andersen Fairy Tales* and a collection of Old Testament Bible stories. Obviously, all dream projects for an illustrator.

But here was something really different and challenging.

To make it even more different I decided to change from my usual technique of watercolour and revert back to my art school days of painting in oils on canvas board. I thought the oils and texture of the canvas would give the work an extra depth and gravitas, a kind of homage to a very special writer.

I can't believe it was 40 years ago!

MELKOR AND UNGOLIANT IN VALINOR
MICHAEL FOREMAN

VARDA OF THE STARS
KIP RASMUSSEN

VARDA

The most beloved of the Valar among Elves and Dwarves was Varda, the maker of the stars. Her importance is shown in her large number of epithets: she is Elentári (star-queen) and Tintallë (star kindler), Quenya titles that translate as Elbereth and Gilthoniel in Sindarin. The white light of the stars is also evoked in other names, such as Fanuilos, meaning "Ever-white".

While her position as queen of the Valar and spouse to Manwë gives Varda a comparable position to the Greek Hera and the Norse Frigg, Tolkien's main inspiration for Varda appears to have come from his own Christian tradition, in the figure of the Virgin Mary. Indeed, in *The Lord of the Rings*, Tolkien's Elvish song "A Elbereth Gilthoniel" – meaning "O Varda the Star-kindler" in Sindarin – has been linked in theme and mood to the Roman Catholic devotional hymn to the Virgin that begins: "Hail, Queen of Heaven, the Ocean Star, / Guide of the wanderer." Varda is called upon by Elves in extremis, just as Roman Catholics call on the Virgin to intercede in times of need.

DRAWING   IAN MILLER

There is never a right place to say this, but drawing is so darn hard.

ULMO

A mighty Vala – Ulmo, Lord of Waters – is second only in his powers to Manwë, Lord of the Air. He dwells in the depths of the sea, rather than in Valinor, and has no spouse. He rarely takes on physical form, but when he does so it is often as a great warrior in silver-green armour with a foam-crested helm, terrible "as a mounting wave that strides to the land." For all that, he is the Vala who is friendliest with the peoples of Middle-earth. He is also closely associated with music, blowing his horns the Ulumúri.

Ulmo has a direct counterpart in the Greek god Poseidon and the Roman Neptune, who were depicted mounted on a giant wave in armour and a chariot drawn by sea horses and accompanied by the merman "old Triton blowing his wreathed horn." In Celtic mythology, Ulmo is most akin to the sea god Manannán mac Lir, with his seaborne chariot. Manannán mac Lir features prominently in the legends of the Tuatha Dé Danaan, though without that god's associations with the Underworld. In Norse mythology, Ulmo is most comparable to Njord.

Interestingly, Ulmo's name may remind us of the Christian martyr Saint Elmo, occasionally spelled Ulmo (d. 303 AD), the patron saint of mariners.

ULMO, LORD OF WATERS
MAURO MAZZARA

MELKOR/MORGOTH

In Tolkien's creation story Ainulindalë, Melkor is the most powerful, inventive and magnificent of the angelic powers known as the Ainur but who, out of his desire to create on his account and in his own way, is corrupted and becomes Morgoth, the first Dark Lord of Middle-earth.

In Tolkien's legendarium, he most resembles the rebel archangel Lucifer of Christian tradition, especially as depicted in John Milton's *Paradise Lost*. Just as the proud Lucifer questions the ways of God, so Melkor asks why the Ainur cannot be allowed to compose their own music and bring forth life and worlds of their own. Both Tolkien's Melkor and Milton's Lucifer are, in one light, heroic in their steadfast "courage never to submit or yield"; however, in truth both rebel angels are primarily motivated by overweening pride and envy.

Setting himself up against the Valar, Melkor builds his fortress of Utumno in the Iron Mountains in the northern wastes of Middle-earth, and digs the foundations of his armoury and dungeon of Angband. Thereafter, Melkor wages five great wars against the Valar. These wars before the rising of the first Moon and Sun and the arrival of Men within the spheres of the world are comparable to the cosmological myths of the ancient Greeks, in which the unruly Titans of the Earth rise up to fight the gods. Ultimately the titanic forces of the Earth are conquered and forced underground, just as Melkor's forces are defeated in those primeval wars with the Valar.

For, as Tolkien explains, Melkor's fall is also a moral one: "From splendour he fell through arrogance to contempt for all things…He began with the desire for Light, but when he could not possess it for himself alone, he descended through fire and wrath into a great burning, down into Darkness." And so, Melkor – like Lucifer – brings corruption into the world. All evil that is, was or will be in Tolkien's world has its beginning in Melkor, but in his beginnings Melkor, again like Lucifer, was not evil.

Just as Melkor was Morgoth's name before his flight from Valinor and return to Middle-earth, Lucifer was Satan's name before his fall in a war of angels in heaven. It was an event recorded in the Gospel of Luke: "I saw Satan fall like lightning from Heaven."

Certainly, by the time of Dante and Milton, Lucifer (meaning "light-bringer") and Satan (meaning "accuser" or "slanderer") had become interchangeable as the name for the Devil. Furthermore, Lucifer, with his biblical epithet "Lucifer son of Morning", was universally recognized as the name for the Morning Star, the brightest "star" in heaven, the planet Venus.

It is of course ironic that Lucifer the bringer of light becomes Satan the bringer of darkness. It is doubly ironic in Tolkien's world, where the Morning Star is the Silmaril carried into the heavens by Eärendil the Mariner, who in the final Great Battle leads the Host of Valar in a war of annihilation against the Dark Enemy and all his allies. And Morgoth, like Satan, is hurled out into the Abyss forever.

OROMË HUNTS THE MONSTERS OF MORGOTH
KIP RASMUSSEN

OROMË AND ARAWN

Oromë, or Araw in Sindarin, is the huntsman of the Valar. He rides his white horse, Nahar, through the forests of Middle-earth as he hunts down the evil creatures of Melkor/Morgoth. Oromë's name means "horn-blower", and the sound of his horn, Valaróma, is a terror to all servants of darkness.

It is fairly certain that Tolkien's inspiration for Oromë was Arawn the Huntsman, a Celtic otherworld deity and the ruler of Annwn, an otherworld of youth and pleasure. Arawn provides an imaginative link between the fictional history of the Elves and the mythological world of the ancient Britons. The Welsh knew this god as Arawn the Huntsman, while Oromë was known to the Sindar (Grey Elves) as Araw the Huntsman. The Welsh Arawn was an immortal huntsman who like Araw/Oromë rode like the wind with horse and hounds through the forests of the mortal world. In the First Branch of the Mabinogi, Arawn the Huntsman befriends the mortal Welsh king, Pwyll, who travels into the immortal Otherworld of Annwn. In the mortal lands of Middle-earth, Araw/Oromë the Huntsman befriends three Elven kings (Ingwë, Finwë and Elwë), who travel to the immortal Undying Lands of Aman.

THE ASTRONOMICAL AND THE MINUTE
KIP RASMUSSEN

It is almost impossible to describe everything that can inspire an illustrator about Tolkien's work, but here are a few of these elements.

His work, for me, starts with the poetry of the imagery. It seems fitting that an author who forged a world in which to place the languages he was creating would write prose so profoundly evocative. We know Tolkien spent much effort in creating poetry proper, but it is the beauty of nearly every prose paragraph that inspires my work. Who else could evoke such visual power in so few words? Here are passages which astound the reader with their economy and magic: the Elves would awaken to the sound of "water falling over stone", and Yavanna would stand in the form of a great tree "crowned with the sun", and the monsters of Morgoth would hunt "silently with many eyes". These brief descriptions are like lightning to an illustrator's creativity.

Moreover, to a visual artist, the scope of the creation is not only astronomical but also minute. What mind can sweep from the creation of the cosmos of Eru to the voice of the waters of Ulmo? All of creation is worthy to Tolkien, from the stars of Varda to the flowers of Samwise the gardener. Trees and moss, stars and song, smithcraft and shipbuilding, architecture, rivers – all are important to that limitless mind.

TULKAS CHAINING MORGOTH
KIP RASMUSSEN

TULKAS THE STRONG

The most valiant and warlike of the Valar, whose name in Quenya simply means "strong". In this respect, Tulkas has a passing resemblance to the Norse god Magni, a name that similarly means strong. However, a closer counterpart can be found in the Greco-Roman Heracles (Hercules), whose primary attribute is his superhuman strength. Both are depicted as supreme wrestlers.

Both Tulkas and Heracles play a key role in cosmic, primordial struggles. Heracles becomes the champion of the gods in the Gigantomachy, killing the giants with his "rushing arrows". Similarly, Tulkas is the "Champion of Valinor", wrestling and overcoming Melkor, after long ages in which the Valar have been unable to contain his powers.

ARDA'S POWERS AT WAR   DAVID DAY

In these images of creation and the shaping of the world, Kip Rasmussen and Mauro Mazzara have excelled in providing spectacular scenes in this titanic struggle between the Powers of Arda. Through their vivid art, we experience something of Tolkien's belief in the importance of the dramatic rendering of this epic struggle between forces that are steadfast and morally upright against those that are corrupted by the pursuit of power for its own sake alone. Through their portrayals of the heroes and heroines of *The Silmarillion* in particular, Rasmussen and Mazzara have helped fulfill Tolkien's wish for "other minds and hands, wielding paint and music and drama" that may be "linked to the majestic whole" of his legendarium.

MAIAR

The lesser angelic powers who descend from the Timeless Halls into Tolkien's world of Arda as servants of the more powerful Valar. The Maiar sometimes have counterparts among the gods, spirits, heroes and nymphs of Greek and Norse mythology but the resemblances are not always clear cut. Thus Eönwë, the herald of Manwë, king of the Valar, is comparable to the Greek Hermes, the herald of Zeus, but has little of the multifaceted, not to say mercurial, nature of Hermes who, among many other roles, also guided the dead to the underworld.

IMAGINING THE DEMIGODS DAVID DAY

Just as Jaroslav Bradac's original line drawings of the Valar were comparable in power and grace to the ancient Greco-Roman and Norse gods; so too Jaroslav's drawings of Maiar spirits had much in common with the demigods and nature spirits of those ancient civilizations. Over the decades many other artists have given us dramatically different interpretations of the Maiar spirits; especially those who entered Arda and aligned themselves with Morgoth the Dark Enemy. These evil Maiar spirits became manifest in monstrous beings, such as the Balrogs, Werewolves, Vampires and Great Spiders.

However, the greatest of the evil Maiar lieutenants of Morgoth to survive the downfall War of Wrath in the First Age was the one known as Gauthar the Cruel. In the Second and Third Ages this was the evil Maia spirit who became the new Dark Lord of Middle-earth. This was Sauron the Ring Lord who established a dark kingdom in the land of Mordor.

MAIAR SPIRITS OF THE SUN, MOON, WAVES AND CALMS JAROSLAV BRADAC

SAURON AND THE EVIL EYE

Sauron is the original Maia spirit of Valinor who was corrupted by Morgoth the Dark Enemy. In the First Age upon Middle-earth, he became known as Sauron Gauthar, meaning "Dread Abomination", or Sauron the Cruel. By the Second Age, Sauron would rise up to become Morgoth's successor as the new Dark Lord of Middle-earth.

In *The Lord of the Rings*, the fiery "Eye of Sauron" is variously described as the "Red Eye", the "Evil Eye", the "Lidless Eye", and the "Great Eye". Tolkien developed this malign manifestation in part out of the tradition of the Evil Eye and imbued it with such a hallucinatory, elemental quality that it has the power to disturb and even terrify the reader and it is the most common visible manifestation of the spirit of the Dark Lord of Mordor in the Third Age.

The Evil Eye was a widespread superstition throughout human history, recorded in ancient Greek and Roman texts as well as many religious scriptures, from the Koran to the Bible, by which an individual, often a sorcerer, has the power to injure or harm by means of a simple, but baleful, glance. Attempts to ward off the power of the evil eye have resulted in the creation of talismans featuring a staring eye, which is supposed to reflect back the malicious gaze on the evildoer. Such talismans are found painted on the prows of boats and ships, on houses and vehicles, and are worn as beads and jewels in a multitude of cultures from the Mediterranean to the Indian Ocean. In all cultures, eyes are believed to have special powers and are said to be windows into the soul.

There is one important mythological source for the Eye. More generally, Odin in his guise as necromancer was the mythological figure who most obviously informed the identity of Sauron the Necromancer and, not coincidentally, was also known as the One-Eyed God. In the Norse canon, Odin sacrificed one of his eyes in exchange for one deep draft from Mirmir's Well, the "Well of Secret Knowledge". Thereafter, Odin – like Sauron – was able to consult with and command wraiths, phantoms and spirits of the dead.

So Tolkien's description of the evil Eye of Sauron gives us considerable insight into the Dark Lord himself: "The Eye was rimmed with fire, but was itself glazed, yellow as a cat's, watchful and intent, and the black slit of its pupil opened on a pit, a window into nothing." This last phrase, "a window into nothing", reflects Tolkien's Roman Catholic, Augustinian philosophical standpoint that evil is essentially the absence of good, and that ultimately evil in itself is a soul-destroying nothingness.

It is difficult to determine whether the spirit of Sauron, after his defeat at the end of the Second Age, was ever able to regain an actual material form – a disembodiment, perhaps, that makes his malign power seem all the greater. Late in the last century of the Third Age, we are given one fearful encounter describing the Dark Lord's four-fingered "Black Hand", but whether this is a phantom shape or the actual material form of the Dark Lord is open to debate. Nonetheless we have it on the authority of Tolkien's son and executor, Christopher Tolkien, that in the War of the Ring it is the Eye that was the Dark Lord's primary manifestation: "father had come to identify the Eye of Barad-dûr with the mind and will of Sauron."

SAURON IN DEFEAT
MAURO MAZZARA

SAURON IN DEFEAT
MAURO MAZZARA

The movies got us used to the fact that Sauron never shows his face. I admit that it's a very good choice for the big screen adaptation, but I really enjoyed drawing the face of this character, as Tolkien describes him as being "beautiful, with fair colours"…I imagined a kind of "über-elf", distorted by the power of the ring. The close-up of the burnt face remains my favourite part, obviously!

THE EYE OF SAURON
JAROSLAV BRADAC

ISTARI

The order of five Wizards, in origin mighty Maiar spirits, who appear in Middle-earth in the Third Age as emissaries of the Valar. Only three of the Istari figure prominently in Tolkien's tales, each named for the colour of his raiment: Saruman the White; Gandalf the Grey; and Radagast the Brown. Tolkien tells us the names of the two others, Alatar and Pallando (together known as the Blue Wizards for their sea-blue cloaks) but that, since they wandered into the far east of Middle-earth, nothing is known of their doings. The meaning of their name (Quenya for "wise ones") may remind us of the biblical Three Wise Men (the Magi), who set out on a journey to visit the infant Jesus.

The Istari have more specific origins in figures from the world's mythologies. Certainly, Gandalf and Saruman, at least, have much in common with Merlin of the Britons, Odin of the Norsemen, Wotan of the ancient Germans, Mercury of the Romans, Hermes of the Greeks and Thoth of the Egyptians. All are linked with magic, sorcery, arcane knowledge and secret doctrine. Most obviously, Merlin, Odin and Wotan commonly took the form of a wandering old man in a traveller's cloak and carrying a staff. And typically – for good or for ill – these disguised deities served as a guide to kings and rulers and often aided them against impossible odds by using their supernatural powers.

GANDALF THE GREY

Gandalf has multiple sources of inspiration in the mythologies of many nations. Most obviously, in appearance, Gandalf, like Merlin, Odin and Wotan, takes on the form of a wandering old man in a grey cloak carrying a staff.

Gandalf's name derives from the Old Icelandic Dvergatal, "Roll of the Dwarves", where it appears as Gandalfr. The two Old Norse elements of Gandalfr are either gand, or gandr, and alf(r). Alf(r) means either "elf" or "white". If the first element is gand, it suggests magical power, while, if it is gandr, it means an object used by sorcerers, such as an enchanted staff.

As to the direct translation of the name Gandalf, then, there are three fairly solid alternatives: "elf wizard", "white staff", and "white sorcerer". All three translations are admirably suitable names for a Wizard. However, Tolkien would likely argue that each translated aspect of this particular Wizard has other definitions hidden within, and we can see how the implications of both layers of meaning played a considerable part in shaping the fate of the character.

The translation "elf wizard" is appropriate because Gandalf is the Wizard most closely associated with the Elves of Middle-earth and the Undying Lands. "White staff" is an apt name as the staff is the primary symbol by which a Wizard is known. The translation of Gandalf as "white wizard", meanwhile, is initially confusing, as his Grey Elven name is Mithrandir, meaning "grey wanderer" (echoed in his common epithet, "the Grey"), and may seem to make the name a more suitable one for Saruman the White. However, this conflict in meaning appears to be a foreshadowing of a twist in plot in which Gandalf the Grey is transformed into Gandalf the White.

In *The Hobbit*, Gandalf appears largely as a standard fairy-tale character: a rather comic, eccentric magician in the company of a band of Dwarves. (He even has something of the character of an absent-

GANDALF THE WHITE
VICTOR AMBRUS

minded history professor about him, of which Tolkien would have had firsthand experience.) Like his fairy-tale counterparts Gandalf also fulfills the traditional role of mentor, adviser and tour guide for the hero and in so doing moves the plot rapidly forward.

Gandalf the Grey certainly fits into this tradition. It is Gandalf who brings the Dwarves and the Hobbit Bilbo Baggins together at the start of the story and sets them on their quest. It is his injection of adventure and magic into the mundane world of the Hobbits that transforms Bilbo Baggins's world. It is Gandalf who leads the band of outlaw adventurers in the form of Thorin and Company to Bilbo's door. It is just this combination of the everyday and the epic that makes *The Hobbit* so compelling. Grand adventures with Dragons, Trolls, Elves and treasure are combined with the afternoon teas, toasted English muffins, pints of ale and smoke-ring-blowing contests.

In *The Hobbit*, then, Gandalf is an amusing and reassuring presence, something like a fairy godfather. In the opening chapter of *The Lord of the Rings*, he seems to reprise the role, appearing much like an odd but much-loved uncle who always amuses everyone with his amateur magic tricks.

A LOVE OF MYTHOLOGY ANDREA PIPARO

I am interested in and passionate about many mythologies, particularly Greek, Nordic and Egyptian, and I am also fascinated by the stories about the life of King Arthur and the medieval era. Magicians and sorcerers such as Gandalf and Merlin have always appealed to me: wise and mystical individuals, their origins shrouded in mystery, often playing the role of counsellors and guides to the young and inexperienced "chosen one" and helping him to fulfill his destiny.

In Norse mythology I recognized, in the figure of Odin, the characteristic traits that probably inspired Tolkien in his creation of the character of Gandalf. Among his many names, Odin was also known as "the wayfarer" as he often used to wander around the earth wearing a grey cloak, an old wide-brimmed hat and leaning on his staff. Another similarity between the sorcerers of Tolkien and Odin are Huginn and Muninn – the two crows that Odin uses to receive news and information from the world. Similarly, Saruman, head of the Istari order, uses crows, the Crebain, to track down the Company and learn about their movements.

Not being a scholar of Tolkien's life, I can only superficially sense what his inspirations were, so more than anything, I consider myself an admirer. Certainly one of the aspects that appeals most in his writings, is how he posits his work as an ancient and exciting legend from ancient times, where the dream that magic may have really existed survives.

TOUCHING ON TOLKIEN IAN MILLER

There and back again, with a few oxbows along the way; in short, a visual and cerebral meander with a "take it easy" sticker on the cerebral.

In the beginning, or perhaps "Once upon a time" is better, I lived in a make believe world, and nobody thought to dissuade me of that fact. Everything, I recall, was a little mixed up boundary wise. Fact and fiction started with an "F" and that was about it. I wanted to be a soldier like my brother, then a railway station, but thinking back in the harsh light of day 60 plus years on, I now suspect that a railway station was then and now beyond my intellectual capacity, and a signal box would have suited me far better? Humility is a wonderful thing when it works.

In the 1950s my mother was a theatrical milliner working for one of the leading London costumiers in Covent Garden, so from the outset I was caught up in the realms of illusion and fantasy. My toy box was a veritable treasure trove of theatrical cast-offs and the remnants from a score of films and theatre productions. Weird and wonderful was the norm and the two "F"s chased each other around the house screaming: "CLARITY!" That was bugger all use to me because I didn't know what it meant. Nearest I got was: it might be something my father drank rather a lot of.

Phantasmagoria and Fata Morgana were not words I was familiar with back then, and in truth, are sometimes forgotten now that I do, but they were always in play back then, as indeed they are today. Medieval and Gothic revelry filled the silver screen, Camelots, Crusader bastions, Norman keeps, crenellated piles of every shape and configuration abounded there; and on a slow day I'd look up at the clouds and search for them there.

Even though I knew that some were little more than paintings on glass, paper cut-outs, and painted structures of wood and canvas, it mattered not a jot. I willingly filled them out with substance and shadows all of mine own. Castles, keeps, almost everything with a defensive wall became an unerring source of fascination for me, as did the people and creatures that occupied them.

I was truly primed for what was to come. It was a "flickering floating world" and I bought into that wholeheartedly. The juxtaposition and interplay of the beautiful and grotesque; the subtle hues, flickering forms and things half seen in a dream or distant memory fitted so well.

Real and unreal were very much in contention, and perhaps still are, if not more so?

SARUMAN AS SHARKEY
IAN MILLER

→

ASTRAL TRAVELLER

Gandalf the Grey's transformation after his battle with the Balrog of Moria is something of a surprise. As the book continues, the force of his personality and ethical purpose increases tenfold as he is revealed as a powerful archetypal Wizard. His later transformation into Gandalf the White is even more shocking. In this, Tolkien seems to be making the point that behind all fairy-tale magicians are the powerful archetypes from myth and epic.

Beyond these relatively straightforward translations of the name, we may contemplate an alternative one for the first element in Gandalf's name: gand, meaning "astral travelling". After falling with the Balrog from the Bridge of Moria, the Wizard's salvation and resurrection seem to come about through a form of astral travelling. As Gandalf the White, the Wizard offers no explanation for his resurrection, but simply states: "I strayed out of thought and time". A better definition of "astral travelling" could not, perhaps, be imagined.

SARUMAN
ANDREW MOCKETT

SARUMAN

Very much in the tradition of Merlin and other Arthurian wizards, Saruman was initially the highest ranked of the order of the Istari. Saruman the White's name in Valinor was Curumo meaning "Cunning One" among the Valar. In the Undying Lands he was (like Sauron) a Maia of Aulë the Smith. Among the Elves he was known as Curunir "Man of Skill", while among Men upon Middle-earth he was known as Saruman. This was a linguistic construct derived from one of two Old English words: "Searomann" meaning "Man of Skill" (a good name for a White Wizard) or the similar "Saroman" meaning "Man of Pain" (a good name for a Black Wizard). Always the philologist, the hidden meanings of Tolkien's names reveal hidden aspects of their character.

Upon arrival in Middle-earth, Saruman was the chief and greatest of the five Istari, but in seeking to overcome the evil power of Sauron, he became seduced by the quest for power itself. Ultimately, his secret desire was to take possession of the One Ring himself and supplant Sauron as the Lord of the Rings. Saruman's tragic tale has much in common with the ancient German legend of Faust, the Magus who became the subject of Christopher Marlowe's *The Tragic History of Doctor Faustus* and Johann Wolfgang von Goethe's *Faust*.

Just as Faust made a bargain with the Devil by exchanging his immortal soul for the promise of unlimited knowledge and worldly power; so Saruman made a bargain with the Dark Lord by exchanging his immortal soul for the promise of unlimited knowledge and worldly power. Treebeard the Ent describes Saruman as having "a mind of metal and wheels" and a fascination with technology, which resulted in the sacrifice of humane values and life itself. Both Faust and Saruman passionately sought knowledge instead of wisdom.

And so the greatest of the Istari who had come to destroy the Dark Lord unwittingly became one of his greatest agents. For just as Faust was deceived by Mephistopheles, so Saruman become the ally and puppet of Sauron the Dark Lord. From his tower of Orthanc in his great ring-walled stronghold of Isengard, Saruman summoned legions of Orcs, Uruk-hai, Half-Orcs and Dunlendings under a black banner marked with a White Hand to make war upon the Men of Rohan and Gondor.

Saruman's influence over others was in good part due to a melodious voice characterized as the "very sound an enchantment" with the power to hold his audience spellbound and enthralled. His speech was also filled with rhetorical tricks, subtle illusions, flattery and charm that combined evil, malice and lies. His speeches had much in common with the enthralling and deceptive discourses of Satan in John Milton's *Paradise Lost*.

PEOPLES RACES AND KINGDOMS

WHERE IT ALL BEGAN   KIP RASMUSSEN

At age eight, I pulled *The Hobbit* from my brother's bookshelf and read the words, "In a hole in the ground there lived a hobbit…" As I read, I realized, even at that age, that this was something like nothing else in the world. I devoured *The Lord of the Rings*, and much later in life read *The Silmarillion*. To me it's one of the greatest works of art in all of history.

HOBBITS

Hobbits, the small, hairy-footed race of Middle-earth, were first introduced to the world with the 1937 publication of Tolkien's novel *The Hobbit*. This rapidly established itself as a children's classic, and its first sentence became arguably one of the best-known opening lines in the history of literature: "In a hole in the ground there lived a hobbit." Curiously, we actually know exactly where and how the first Hobbit made its appearance in his creator's mind. On a warm summer afternoon in 1930, Tolkien was sitting at his desk in his study at 20 Northmoor Road in the suburbs of Oxford. He was engaged in the "everlasting weariness" of marking school certificate papers, when "on a blank leaf [he] scrawled 'In a hole in the ground there lived a hobbit." Tolkien "did not […] know why."

Tolkien was a professor of Anglo-Saxon and a philologist. He had worked as a scholar on the *Oxford English Dictionary* and knew the English language (and a multitude of other languages) to its very roots. Words – the look and feel of them as well as their origins – inspired him. Of that moment when the word "hobbit" first came to him, he commented: "Names always generate a story in my mind. Eventually I thought I'd better find out what hobbits were like. But that was only a beginning." Indeed, "only a beginning" is a profound understatement.

Tolkien really did start with the word "Hobbit". It became a kind of riddle that needed solving. He decided that he must begin by inventing a philological origin for the word as a worn-down form of an original invented word, holbytla (which is actually an Anglo-Saxon or Old English construct), meaning "hole builder". The opening line of the novel-to-be, therefore, was an obscure lexicographical joke and a weird piece of circular thinking: "In a hole in the ground there lived a hole builder".

This is an unusual way to develop a character and write a novel, but it was clearly an essential part of Tolkien's creative process. Nearly all aspects of Hobbit life and adventure seem to evolve from their given names, which themselves dictate the direction of the story, as witnessed above all in the stories of Tolkien's greatest Hobbit heroes, Bilbo and Frodo Baggins.

HOLMAN GREENHAND
LIDIA POSTMA

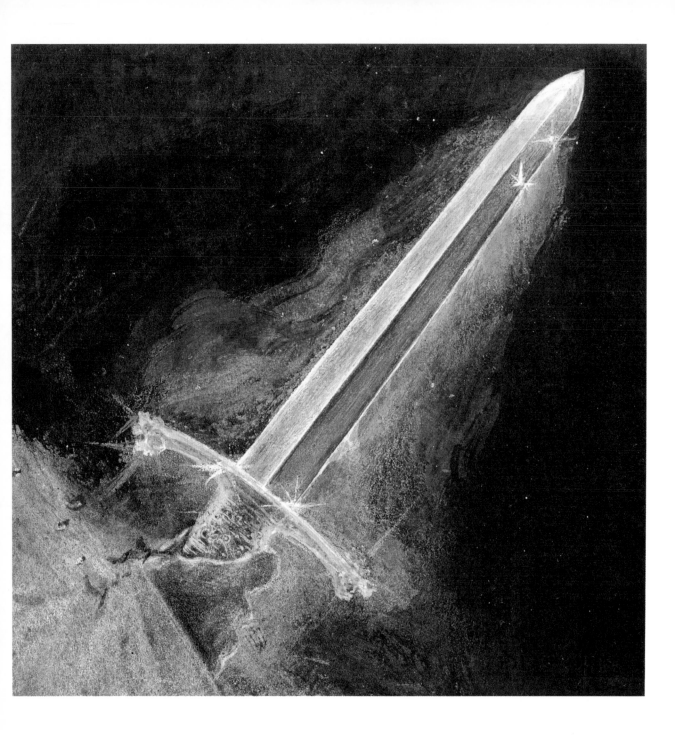

STING
LIDIA POSTMA

←———————

BILBO BAGGINS

Bilbo Baggins was the first and original Hobbit created by Tolkien, the comic anti-hero of the eponymous *The Hobbit* who goes off on a journey into a heroic world. It is a world where the commonplace collides with the heroic, where the corresponding values clash to entertaining effect. In Bilbo Baggins, we have a character with whose everyday sensibilities the reader may identify, while vicariously having an adventure in a heroic world.

As Tolkien often observed, "names often generate a story"; they also nearly always contributed and suggested something of the nature or character of the person, place or thing named. Another aspect of Bilbo Baggins's character may be revealed by an analysis of his first name. The word "bilbo" entered into the English language in the late sixteenth century as the name for a short but deadly piercing sword of the kind once made in the northern Spanish port-city of Bilbao, from whence the name.

This is an excellent description of Bilbo's sword, the charmed Elf knife called Sting. Found in a Troll hoard, Bilbo's "bilbo" can pierce through armour or animal hide that would break any other sword. In *The Hobbit*, however, it is our hero's sharp wit rather than his sharp sword that gives Bilbo the edge. In his bids to escape Orcs, Elves, Gollum or the Dragon, Bilbo's well-honed wits allow him to solve riddles, trick villains and generally get himself out of sticky situations.

When we put the two names together as Bilbo Baggins, we have two aspects of our hero's character and to some degree the character of Hobbits in general. On the face of it, the name Baggins suggests a harmless, well-to-do, contented character (though with criminal undertones!), while the name Bilbo suggests an individual who is sharp, intelligent and even a little dangerous.

HOBBITS AND DUTCH MASTERS
DAVID DAY

Although the Hobbits were among the last of the races to appear in the chronologies of Middle-earth, they were the first race of Tolkien's world that most readers encountered through the publication of his first novel, *The Hobbit*. The remarkable Dutch artist Lidia Postma has been our chief illustrator of Hobbits. As the recipient of numerous international awards for her illustrations of her own fairy tales and those of Hans Christian Andersen, Lidia's atmospheric and character driven portrayals of Hobbits draw on her deep heritage as a Dutch artist. Lidia's illustration *Shire Society*, portraying Bilbo Baggins's eleventy-first birthday, is something of a tribute to the crowded peasant village scenes of the Dutch masters Pieter Bruegel the Elder and his son Pieter Bruegel the Younger.

BAGGINS AND BAGGERS

Baggins was the family name of Tolkien's principal Hobbit heroes in *The Hobbit* and *The Lord of the Rings*. It derives from a double source – the English Somerset surname Bagg, meaning "money-bag" or "wealthy", and the term "baggins", meaning "afternoon tea or snack between meals" – and is certainly appropriate for a prosperous and well-fed Hobbit.

Initially, the "original Hobbit", Bilbo Baggins, is presented as a mildly comic, home-loving, rustic, middle-class "gentle-Hobbit". He seems harmless and placid enough, if given to a little irritability, and full of gossip, homespun wisdom, wordy euphemisms and elaborate family histories. He is largely concerned with domestic comforts, village fetes, dinner parties, flower gardens, vegetable gardens and grain harvests. However, once recruited by Thorin and his Dwarf Company, the respectable Bilbo Baggins is revealed – much to his own astonishment – to be a highly skilled master burglar.

Tolkien always maintained that his tales were often inspired by names and words, and indeed, in the jargon of the nineteenth- and early twentieth-century criminal underworld there is a cluster of terms around "bag" and "baggage" that link up with one or other of the various highly specialized forms of larceny. Three are especially noteworthy: "to bag" means to capture, to acquire or to steal; a "baggage man" is the outlaw who carries off the loot or booty; and a "bagman" is the man who collects and distributes money on behalf of others by dishonest means or for dishonest purposes.

It appears, then, that the name Baggins not only helped to create the character of Tolkien's Hobbit hero, but also went a long way toward plotting the adventure his hero embarks on. For, in *The Hobbit*, we discover a Baggins who is hired by Dwarves to bag the Dragon's treasure. He then becomes a baggage man who carries off the loot. However, after the death of the Dragon and because of a dispute after the Battle of the Five Armies, the Baggins Hobbit becomes the bagman who collects the whole treasure together and distributes it among the victors.

Along with the Baggins name, further "baggage" is passed on to Bilbo's heir, Frodo Baggins. In the context of the One Ring, there is a link between the name Baggins and another specialized underworld occupation: the bagger or bag thief. This bagger or bag thief has nothing to do with baggage, but was derived from the French *bague*, meaning "ring". A bagger, then, is a thief who specializes in stealing rings by seizing a victim's hand and stripping it of its rings. It appears to have been in common usage in Britain's criminal underworld between about 1890 and 1940.

SMAUG AND THE HOBBIT   MAURO MAZZARA

Smaug is probably just the best subject ever, no? Proud, arrogant, evil, mean, beautiful, charming, smart… and last but not least…he's a *dragon*! He is the super top model of fantasy! I just enjoyed painting it – pure fun – adding details, imagining treasure pieces, making the Hobbit as small and defenceless as I could. The colours are simple: yellow tones, golden glazes everywhere and a violet that goes to black, to show how big and magnificent the halls under the mountain were.

FRODO AND SAM IN MORDOR
LIDIA POSTMA

THE MASTER-SERVANT RELATIONSHIP

In Old English and Scandinavian mythology, the name Frodo (or Froda, Frothi, Frotha) is most often connected with a peacemaker. In the Old English epic of *Beowulf* there is Froda the powerful King of the Heathobards who attempts to make peace between Danes and Bards. In Norse mythology there is a King Frothi who rules a realm of peace and prosperity.

Samwise Gamgee, Frodo's companion and servant throughout the Quest of the Ring, was what Tolkien called a typical "plain unimaginative, parochial" Hobbit. Yet his deeds also displayed what Tolkien described as the most unlikely Hobbit characteristic of the "amazing and unexpected heroism of ordinary men 'at a pinch'". In a personal letter in 1956, Tolkien wrote that a good part of his characterization of his fictional Samwise Gamgee was derived from his experience as a signals officer in the First World War. "My Samwise is indeed largely a reflection of the English soldier – grafted on the village-boys of early days, the memory of the privates and my batmen that I knew in the 1914 War, and recognized as so far superior to myself." (Batmen were soldiers who were essentially manservants to British officers.) In the First World War, British officers were from the upper-middle classes, or – as was Tolkien – university-educated men. Working-class men were recruited as privates and could only ascend to the rank of sergeant. Sam was a humble uneducated gardener and employee of the Master of Bag End.

The relationship between Frodo and Samwise was very much that of an Edwardian master and servant. Although not uncritical of the class structure and customs of that time, Tolkien was enough of an Edwardian himself to believe that within these roles a bond of mutual respect and loyalty to each other was possible and could be an ennobling thing. John Garth, the author of *Tolkien in the Great War*, has observed that as the quest progressed, the master–servant relationship largely became inverted: "[Frodo] presents the problems, Sam the solutions." And, that in the First World War "this process was far from atypical." It was a view that Tolkien observed and recognized in the fog of war that his batsmen might often prove "far superior to myself."

FRODO AND SAM   LIDIA POSTMA

Tolkien let his imagination run free and furnished it with everything he liked or hated and with all the knowledge he acquired about whatever subject fascinated him. He created a godless universe as the stage for his farce-like tragedy or tragic farce, starting with a plain personage: a Hobbit. And that Hobbit is "me", or "I". Because this is the genial ploy – we identify with the Hobbits, not with Tolkien's men or any other species. The diminutive size of the Hobbit makes him endearing, and at the same time he is the ideal escape. The way children escape the seriousness of the adult life of men, while playing out all the grave issues of life. Tolkien's work of art is, and always will be, for grown-up children and this is exactly the audience an illustrator needs for *his* similarly furnished universe. It is an endless playground for the fantasy artist.

PORTRAITS MAURO MAZZARA

Today I have the luck to work as an illustrator with different kind of clients, from fiction to non-fiction. I love to realize portraits and I really enjoyed drawing the portraits of the Hobbits. Usually, I draw portraits of real people but this time I was drawing people who only exist in my mind. Following the descriptions of the three breeds of Hobbits, and without having the easy get-out of being able to focus on their feet, or their size side-by-side, I tried instead to portray their manner, characteristics and feelings.

FEET IAN MILLER

I was at Art school for seven years. My shoe size changed in that period but I did not develop hairy Hobbit feet. I'm still not sure why it took so long; I got a painting degree. After a year in the sculpture department, I left in 1970 and found work as an illustrator. That is where I re-engaged with the world of Tolkien again.

HARFOOTS

The smallest in stature and most typical of the three strains of Hobbits: the standard-issue diminutive, brown-skinned, curly-haired, hairy-footed, hole-dwelling Hobbit. The other two Hobbit breeds are the Fallohide and Stoor. Together, these three races were meant to link the history of the Hobbits with that of the Germanic settlers of Britain: the Saxons, the Angles and the Jutes. The Harfoots were most likely to trade with Dwarves, while the Fallohides were most likely to consort with Elves, and the Stoors with Men.

Harfoot is in fact a English surname derived from the Old English *haer-fot* ("hare-foot"), meaning "fast runner" or "nimble as a hare". The best-known historic individual to bear this name was Harold Harefoot, who became Harold I (reigned 1035–40), one of the last Saxon kings. The association of Hobbits with hares not only implies nimbleness, but also keen sight and hearing, as well as oversized feet. Also there is the implied pun on "hair-foot", referring to the Hobbits' distinctively furry feet. Together all these allusions provide a succinct description of this Hobbit kind: a small, nimble creature with large, hairy feet. Typical Harfoot surnames are: Brown, Brownlock, Sandheaver, Tunnelly, Burrows, Gardner, Hayward and Roper.

HARFOOT HOBBIT
MAURO MAZZARA

STOOR HOBBIT AND FALLOHIDE HOBBIT
MAURO MAZZARA

STOORS

The largest and strongest of three Hobbit breeds and the most like humans. The Stoors were the first Hobbits to live in houses, and they tend to dwell near rivers and marshes. They are also the only Hobbits to use footwear (usually Dwarf boots) and to be capable of growing any kind of beard or facial hair. Stoors also distinguish themselves by being the only breed that is unafraid of water or even considers the idea of boating and swimming. Through their commerce on the river, the Stoors are among the wealthiest of Hobbits.

The name "Stoor" appears to be appropriately derived from the Middle English "stur" and the Old English "stor", meaning hard or strong. It also suggests "store" in the sense of being merchants, but even more in the sense that all Hobbits are hoarders with many storage spaces and rooms in their Hobbit holes or houses. Typical Stoorish names include Banks, Puddifoot, Cotton and Cotman.

FALLOHIDES

The least numerous and the most unconventional of the three kindreds of Hobbit, in origin woodland-dwelling and thus most friendly with the Elves. Usually the tallest and slimmest of their race, they are commonly fair-skinned, fair-haired, and most likely to go on adventures. Almost any display of individuality or ambition exhibited by a normally conventional Hobbit is usually attributed to a distant Fallohide bloodline.

The name Fallohide provides some of the inspiration for the character Tolkien gives to this kindred. "Falo" is an Old High German word meaning "pale yellow" (as in the colour of a fallow deer), and "hide", of course, is a skin or pelt, and so together is descriptive of the outward appearance of the Fallohides. "Fallow", meanwhile, is also Old English for "newly ploughed land", and "hide" is an Old English measure of land sufficient for a household (about 40,4686m^2 [100 acres]). This second derivation suggests the characteristics shared by all Hobbits: a love of newly tilled land and an uncanny ability to hide away in the landscape, so as to appear almost invisible to Men. Furthermore, one cannot help but think that there is yet another layer of wordplay with "Follow and Hide" as a Hobbitish version of the game of Hide and Seek. Typically fair-haired Fallohide family names are Fairbairn, Goold and Goldworthy, while their unconventional, independent nature and their intelligence are suggested by such names as Headstrong and Boffin.

ELVES
VICTOR AMBRUS

ELVES

In Tolkien's world, Elves were in large part inspired by the author's wish to give precise definition to a multitude of lost traditions and mythologies relating to supernatural beings known as "Elfs" which, in the passage of history, had been reduced to little more than the pixies, flower-fairies, sprites and gnomes of English folklore and Victorian children's stories. Tolkien came to the rescue of these long-lost traditions and revived them again in the pages of literature. In the writing of *The Silmarillion*, Tolkien gave life and context to the millennia-long histories of over 40 races, nations, kindreds and city-states of Elves.

Tolkien began his "rescue" of the Elves by clarifying matters linguistically, just as he had done with his Dwarves: "Elfs" became "Elves" and "Elfin" became "Elven". Tolkien wished to define the "Elf" as a distinct and singularly important race. The word "elf" means white, related to the alba and Greek alphos (both meaning white), and also retains an association with "swan". It is through this tracking back to the roots of language that Tolkien's Elves gradually re-emerged from the ancient legends of Britain, originally known as Albion (a name possibly related to the Indo-Euopean root *albho*, or white), which Tolkien implies could be literally translated as "Elf-land".

We know that Tolkien also looked to Norse mythology for the history of his Elves. In Norse mythology, there are references to both the light elfs of Alfheim ("elf home") and the rather sinister dark elfs of the subterranean Svartalfheim ("black elf home"). Tolkien took this somewhat mysterious division and used it to create the first great event in the history of his Elves: the "Sundering of the Elves" after their awakening by Cuiviénen, between the Calaquendi ("Light-Elves") who made the journey to Eldamar (meaning "elven home") and the Moriquendi ("Dark-Elves") who refused the journey and remained under the starlight in the east of Middle-earth, never seeing the divine Trees of Light in the Undying Lands.

Above all, it should be stressed that Tolkien's Elves are not a race of pixies. They are a powerful, full-blooded people who closely resemble the prehuman Irish race of immortals called the Tuatha Dé Danann. Like the Tuatha Dé Danann, Tolkien's Elves are taller and stronger than mortals, are incapable of suffering sickness, are possessed of more-than-human beauty, and are filled with greater wisdom in all things. Tolkien took the sketchy myths and legends of the Tuatha Dé Danann and created a vast civilization, history and genealogy for his Elves. He gave them a rich family of languages and a vast cultural inheritance that, for all that it was rooted in real traditions, required all his genius and imagination to truly flourish.

ELVES AND CELTS
DAVID DAY

The elder statesman of our illustrators is Victor Ambrus. By the time we began gathering artists for *A Tolkien Bestiary*, Victor had already been elected a Fellow of the Royal Society of Artists (FRSA) and published nine books, including the two (also written by him) that won the Kate Greenaway Medal for the best British children's book illustrator of the year. Since that time, Victor has written and illustrated 30 of his own books, and illustrated well over 300 other books by other authors.

One of Britain's most respected and prolific illustrators, Victor Ambrus has in recent years gained considerable popularity as the artist in the *Time Team* TV series on archaeological reconstructions.

Because of his deep historical knowledge, Victor was commissioned specifically to create a score of otherworldly Celtic portrayals of Tolkien's many races and tribes of the immortal Elves. It was no simple task to create line drawing images of a race that was stronger, nobler, wiser and more beautiful than humans. Victor's black and white images give a continuity and immediately recognizable identity to Elves throughout the series. From the golden-haired peaceful Vanyar Fair Elves to the dark-haired warlike Noldor Deep-Elves to the adventurous roving Teleri Sea-Elves and the many wandering tribes and nations of forest-dwelling Sylvan-Elves.

IMMORTAL ENCOUNTERS   KIP RASMUSSEN

"Being filled with love Elwë came to her and took her hand, and straightway a spell was laid on him, so that they stood thus while long years were measured by the wheeling stars above them; and the trees of Nan Elmoth grew tall and dark before they spoke any word."

What a passage, what a scene! What kind of person would I have been to change anything Tolkien wrote about this immortal encounter? It became supremely important to me to try to make this moment as beautiful as I could. I had previously spent several years studying the principles of Japanese gardens and tried to include everything I loved about the natural world, but which would still be consistent with Tolkien's description. This included trees, rocks, waterfalls and the nightingales of Melian which flit just behind her. But, most of all, the colour scheme of that age had to be illuminated only by the stars of Varda.

MELIAN AND THINGOL

Name taken by the Telerin Elwë, as the silver-haired king of the Sindarin, or Grey Elves, and founder of the forest kingdom of Doriath, where he rules alongside his wife, the Maia Melian. In his own right and as the father of Lúthien, he is a key figure in the tales of Beleriand in the First Age.

Some of the events in his history echo those in myths and legends. His enchantment and disappearance after he meets Melian in the forest of Nan Elmoth recalls the enchantment and imprisonment of Merlin by Vivien in Arthurian legend. There is an important distinction, however. In Tolkien the enchantment arises out of mutual love – almost like a coup de foudre – while Vivien, in most versions at least, acts out of hatred.

Likewise, Thingol's refusal to give Lúthien in marriage to Beren, unless the latter succeeds in what seems the impossible task of retrieving a Silmaril from the iron crown of Morgoth, echoes any number of myths and fairy tales in which a jealous or fearful father prevents his daughter from marrying. We find the motif, for example, in the medieval Welsh legend Culhwch and Olwen, and in Greek mythology in the story of Pelops and Hippodameia, whose father, Oenomaus, will only allow a suitor to marry his daughter if he can beat him in a (rigged) chariot race.

Thingol's death at the hands of the Dwarves of Nogrod, in a conflict over a beautiful necklace, returns us to the brutal world of Norse mythology.

MELIAN AND THINGOL
KIP RASMUSSEN

LÚTHIEN FINDS BEREN
KIP RASMUSSEN

← —→

PEOPLE OF THE STARS   DAVID DAY

Kip Rasmussen's dramatic full-colour portrayals of events in the early history of the Elves manage to capture the enchantment of Tolkien's People of the Stars. There is a wonderful sense of amazement conveyed in his *Oromë Finds the Lords of the Elves* in the Ages of Starlight. These were the First Born Children of Ilúvatar awakened by the light of the stars. And in his *Lúthien Finds Beren* and *Melian and Thingol*, Kip captures other historic moments of enchantment when royal lovers first meet in *The Silmarillion*.

LÚTHIEN AND BEREN

Beren was one of the Edain (men) and was one of the greatest heroes of the First Age of Middle-earth, and the character whose story (along with that of Beren's beloved, Lúthien) was most meaningful to Tolkien himself. So great was the author's identification with the hero that he had the names Lúthien and Beren included beneath his wife Edith's and his own on their shared gravestone in Wolvercote Cemetery in Oxford.

Beren Erchamion and Lúthien Tinúviel are the central protagonists in the Quest for the Silmaril, the story of a mortal man's quest for the hand of an immortal Elf-maid.

Lúthien ("Maiden of Twiglight") is daughter of Thingol, the high king of the Grey Elves and his queen, Melian the Maia, considered the most beautiful child of any race and the fairest singer within the spheres of the world, around whom nightingales gathered. Lúthien, like Galadriel, is another embodiment of the "lady in white" of Celtic legend, though here there seems to be a direct inspiration in the figure of Olwyn, whose eyes, like Lúthien's, shine with light and whose skin is also as white as snow. Both figures are closely associated with flowers: Lúthien with the white star-shaped flower Niphredil and Olwyn with the white trefoil or clover.

As in many myths, legends and fairy tales, the hero must prove his worthiness by achieving an impossible task, often set by the heroine's father, who believes that the hero will die in the attempt. Here it is King Thingol who sets Beren the task of retrieving a Silmaril, set into the crown of Morgoth, who dwells in the evil fortress of Angband. To Thingol's horror, Lúthien sets out on the quest alongside her beloved Beren.

LÚTHIEN DANCES BEFORE MORGOTH
TURNER MOHAN

As Tolkien freely acknowledged, the subsequent development of the tale was closely patterned on the Greek myth of Orpheus and Eurydice, only with the male and female roles reversed. In the myth, the musician Orpheus attempts to bring Eurydice back from the dead. Making his descent into the underworld, Orpheus plays his harp and sings to make the three-headed hound Cerberus, who guards the gates of hell, fall asleep. Brought before Hades, king of the underworld, Orpheus again plays and sings so beautifully that the god is moved to grant him the life of Eurydice, on condition that he does not look back at her as they make their way back into the land of the living. At the last moment, at the mouth of the tunnel, Orpheus cannot resist looking back at his beloved and she is taken from him and returned to Hades forever.

In Tolkien, it is Lúthien who, when the lovers reach the gates of the underworld-like fortress of Angband, lulls its unsleeping guardian, the gigantic wolf Carcharoth. It is she, too, who lulls Morgoth – the king of this underworld – to sleep (rather than moving him), enabling Beren to prize one of the Silmarils from Morgoth's crown. Like Orpheus and Eurydice, Tolkien's lovers fail at the last hurdle when Carcharoth wakes before the lovers can make their escape. At this point in the narrative, Tolkien departs from the Greek tale and introduces an allusion to the Norse legend of Fenrir, the Great Wolf of Midgard, who bites off the hand of the god Tyr when the gods bind him. Carcharoth, too, bites off Beren's hand and swallows both the hand and the Silmaril he is holding. It is from this episode that Beren gains the epithet Erchamion, meaning "One Handed".

To underscore the connection between the Greek myth and his tale, Tolkien duplicates the descent into the underworld motif by having Lúthien pursue Beren's soul after his death. This time, in the House of the Dead in the Undying Lands, Lúthien exactly repeats Orpheus' journey by singing to Mandos, the Doomsman of the Valar (a figure comparable to the Greek Hades), and winning from him a second life for her lover. Unlike Orpheus and Eurydice, however, Lúthien and Beren are allowed to live out their newly won mortal lives quietly. Thus, in the Quest for the Silmaril, Tolkien not only reversed the roles of Orpheus and Eurydice, but also overturned that story's tragic end. In so doing, for a time at least, Tolkien allowed love to conquer death.

OROMË FINDS THE LORDS OF THE ELVES
KIP RASMUSSEN

FËANOR
VICTOR AMBRUS

ON CHARACTER
KIP RASMUSSEN

I believe that some of Tolkien's most memorable characters are also partial descriptions of the character of the author. Tolkien is, in part, Gandalf, who as Olórin, "would walk among the Elves unseen and they would not know whence came the fair visions that he put into their hearts." Tolkien spent his life encouraging us to do good both simply and heroically. He is also Fëanor (without the catastrophic pride) who was "driven by the fire of his own heart, working ever swiftly (relatively speaking) and alone." And he is Eru, who propounded his panoramic visions but invited others to sing in creation with the themes he set out.

Character traits such as these are a treasure trove to depict: the strength and pride of Fëanor and Túrin, the goodness and courage of Melian and Lúthien, the treachery of Maeglin, the sacrifice of Finrod and Barahir, and the resolve and friendship of Frodo and Sam.

DURIN IN THE LONG SLEEP
KIP RASMUSSEN

THE SLEEPER

Durin the Deathless is the first king of the Longbeards, one of the seven kindreds of Dwarves. The Longbeards – with whom Tolkien's histories of the Dwarves of Middle-earth are largely concerned – are more commonly known as Durin's Folk in honour of their first king.

The name Durin (or Durinn) is first recorded in the Icelandic Prose Edda, in the Dvergatal, or "Dwarf's Roll". The name translates as "The Sleeper" or "Sleepy" and is the key to Tolkien's inspiration in his creation story of the "Seven Fathers of the Dwarves", otherwise known as the "Seven Sleepers". In *The Silmarillion* the first Dwarves are shaped by Aulë the Smith but, on the command of Eru, are kept sleeping "under stone" until awakened when the dark skies are filled with starlight by Varda.

As the founder of the greatest Dwarf kingdom of Khazad-dûm in the Misty Mountains, King Durin I is known as "Durin the Deathless", though only in part because he is very long-lived. Tolkien's Dwarves have a messianic belief – not unlike real-world beliefs about spiritual leaders – that each king who carries the name Durin is actually a reincarnation of the original Father of the Longbeards. It is an article of faith among the Longbeards that this mysterious cycle spanning many ages will end only with the seventh and final incarnation, Durin VII, who will appear at some undisclosed time in Middle-earth's future ages.

Despite wars and conflicts over the millennia, Durin's Folk prospered well until the year 1980 of the Third Age of the Sun when the Dwarves of Khazad-dûm by chance or fate delved too deep in their mines and awoke a monstrous demon of fire. This is an ancient Maia fire spirit known as a Balrog or Valaraukar, meaning "demon of might". The source of Tolkien's inspiration for this monster is the Norse fire giant Surt who was the Lord of Muspelheim, the evil volcanic underworld domain of fire. In Middle-earth, this Balrog with his flaming sword and "scourges of fire" slew King Durin VI and drove Durin's folk from Khazad-dûm.

This disaster marked the beginning of the diaspora of Durin's Folk. Driven from their ancient kingdom – renamed Moria, meaning "Black Chasm" – the Longbeards were constantly on the move, exiles in search of a safe new realm. But in the Third Age the terrors that lurked in the scattered realms of Durin's Folk also endanger the kingdoms of the Dúnedain. The Balrog in Moria, Orcs in the Misty Mountains and Dragons in the Grey Mountains and Erebor not only threatened the Dwarves of Durin's Folk, but all the Free Peoples of Middle-earth. And so, in the Dúnedain of Arnor and Gondor, Durin's Dwarves became natural allies in the War of the Ring as recounted in Tolkien's *The Lord of the Rings*.

THE COMPANY OF DWARVES
LIDIA POSTMA

DVERGATAL AND THE NAMING OF DWARVES

The Dvergatal (or the "dwarf's roll") is a list of the names of mythological dwarfs found in the Icelandic twelfth-century text known as the Prose Edda on which Tolkien drew for many of his Dwarvish names. All the Dwarves in *The Hobbit* appear in this list: Thorin, Dwalin, Balin, Kili, Fili, Bifur, Bofur, Bombur, Dori, Nori, Ori, Óin and Glóin. Other names of dwarfs which Tolkien also found in the Dvergatal, and which he used later, include: Thráin, Thrór, Dáin and Náin. The Dvergatal, however, was not only a fruitful source of names but also an inspiration for Tolkien in creating the characters and backgrounds of his Dwarves.

Thorin's father, Thráin, meaning "stubborn", is slain while stubbornly resisting Dragon invasions of his realm. Thorin's sister and, interestingly, the only named female Dwarf in Tolkien's works, is named Dis, which simply means "Sister". Unlike most of the male Dwarves – whose names mean or reflect a personal attribute – Dis, the "Sister" is solely identified by her family position in relation to Thorin. Thorin's heir, Dáin II, known as Ironfoot, proves true to his warrior name ("deadly") when he and several hundred Dwarves come to Thorin's aid in the Battle of the Five Armies. The names of other members of the Thorin's Company were instrumental in Tolkien's shaping of their characters. Bombur, meaning "Bulging", is certainly the fattest of the Dwarves, and Nori, meaning "Peewee", is the smallest; Balin, meaning "Burning One", is fiery in battle, but warm with his friends; Ori, meaning "Furious", fights furiously before he is slain in Moria; and Glóin, meaning "Glowing One", wins glory and riches. There seems little doubt, then, that the Dvergatal was a rich inspiration for Tolkien and the means by which he "discovered" the characters of his Dwarves.

THE ARCHETYPAL AND THE UNIQUE

IAN MILLER

Tolkien's *The Hobbit* and Ring Trilogy, along with Mervyn Peake's *Gormenghast*, seemed so familiar when I read them for the first time, almost in tandem as it happens, that it almost hurt. I all but toppled into them, as one might accidentally fall into a fast-flowing river, thereafter to be swept along at a frightful pace in awe of both the flow and passing scenery, narrative notwithstanding. Rush though it was, I'm happy to say I floated well and enjoyed every moment of that literary immersion.

I have touched on the subject of the "Northern European Tradition" many times over the years, and believe it touches at the roots of each succeeding generation, providing a well of stored and shared memories, into which we all dip occasionally, sometimes knowingly, other times subconsciously. If this is in actuality nothing more than the function of Folklore and History, then so be it.

I think both Tolkien and Peake tapped into this well with astonishing success, and this perhaps explains the unnerving familiarity I previously mentioned having experienced with the worlds they conjured up, archetypal, despite the unique nature of the literary weaves they created.

DWARF WITH AXE ↑

IAN MILLER

SHADOWY PLACES   IAN MILLER

Despite a love of colour and light, I have always felt a strong attraction for the mist, shadowy places, the stark skeletal qualities of winter and the sough of the gelid winds that blow then; even though I've been heard on occasion to scream for a bit of blue sky and sunshine. The filigree of the bare treetop branches set against a troubled sky with a rook or crow perched in amongst them is a delight, and for as long as I can remember I've been putting black specks in my pictures and always will.

Castle keeps with corvids toppling from the sky like burnt paper. What could be better?

DEEP-DELVING DWARVES   DAVID DAY

Just as Victor Ambrus was commissioned to specifically create line drawings of Elves in a distinctive style, so Ian Miller was commissioned to create unique and definitive line drawings of Dwarves that would give a continuity and immediately recognizable identity to Dwarves throughout the series. Just as Ambrus's Elves were blessed with beauty and immortality as they walked and sang in their enchanted woods under bright stars, so Miller's Dwarves were dark and brooding inhabitants of underground kingdoms and caverns as they toiled in their mines in a never-ending search for the treasures of the earth. Ian Miller's portrayal of Dwarves was exactly right for *The Lord of the Rings* and *The Silmarillion*, but was rather too sinister to entirely fit in with what are essentially children's fairy tale Dwarves in *The Hobbit*.

THORIN AND COMPANY
ANDREA PIPARO

←———←

DWARVES

Tolkien's doughty race of Dwarves in Middle-earth was inspired by Norse and other Germanic tales of a powerful but stunted subterranean race that lived within mountain kingdoms: masters of fire and forge, makers of weapons and jewels, guardians of treasures and bestowers of magical gifts. Dissatisfied with the portrayal of dwarfs in popular fairy tales as diminutive, rather comic creatures, Tolkien set out to create a race that was altogether more ambivalent, at times even sinister.

The reader's initial impression of the Dwarves of Thorin and Company in *The Hobbit* is largely consistent with the dwarfs of the mildly comic fairy-tale variety. Even within the course of that book, however, the Dwarves seem to "grow in stature" and take on more heroic attributes. It is in *The Silmarillion*, though, that they most fully reveal their true nature as a dark and brooding race with the fatalistic character of the dwarf-smiths of Norse mythology. Indeed, Tolkien's Dwarves are comparable – in all but size – to the Norsemen of Scandinavia: a proud race of warriors, craftsmen and traders. Stoic and stubborn, both Dwarves and Norsemen are alike in their admiration of strength and bravery, in their sense of honour and loyalty, and in their love of gold and treasure. They are all but identical in their skill in the wielding and forging of weapons, in their stubborn pride and their determination to avenge perceived injustice.

However brave and fearless Tolkien's Dwarves are on their own ground (underground), they are mistrustful, dismissive and fearful of all that they do not know. Unlike the Norsemen, they hate the open sea, deep forests and wide plains. They would rather burn a boat than sail in it, cut down a tree than climb it, and carry a horse than ride it. Dwarves only find security in the deep roots of mountains and joy in the working of gold and precious metals, the forging of steel, the carving of stone and the setting of gems.

Ultimately, however, we find that Tolkien remains largely consistent with ancient folk tradition: his Dwarves are the genies of the mountains, just as Hobbits are the genies of tilled soil and farmlands, and Ents are the genies of the forests. Through his research, Tolkien felt that he was able to understand fully the true nature and character of this secretive, stunted, mountain-dwelling race.

THORIN OAKENSHIELD   DAVID DAY

Andrea Piparo was among those illustrators who have produced portraits of Thorin Oakenshield and his Company of adventurers in their Quest of Lonely Mountain. Ian Miller's Dwarves conveyed the primeval creatures of Norse mythology that inspired Tolkien's Dwarves of *The Silmarillion*; while Andrea Piparo's Dwarves were more akin to those to be found in Grimm's tales and modern variations of *Snow White and the Seven Dwarfs*. Kip Rasmussen's dramatic entombed Durin in *Durin in the Long Sleep* certainly conveys the powerful origin myth of the first and greatest of the Seven Fathers of the Dwarves. But Andrea Piparo's Thorin Oakenshield, as the distant direct descendant of Durin the Deathless, successfully conveys something of his ancestors' evolution into the more down-to-earth, treasure-hungry fairy-tale Dwarf king.

MORTAL MEN

Tolkien's tale of the origin of Men in the east of Middle-earth and their westward migration in the Years of the Sun was a mirroring of the origin and migration of the Elves in the Years of the Trees. And, just as Tolkien's journey of the Elves was inspired by the tales related to the historic westward migrations of Celtic peoples, it can also be observed that his journey of Men was inspired by the historic westward migrations of the Teutonic peoples.

Consequently, just as the immortal Elves were aligned with the myths and folk traditions of the Celts, Tolkien's mortal Men were equally aligned with the myths and folk traditions of the Germans, Norsemen and Anglo-Saxons. The dominant language of the Elves of Beleriand was Sindarin, modelled on Welsh, while the dominant Mannish language of the Edain – those heroic Men of the First Age who entered Beleriand first – was Taliska, the ancestor of Tolkien's Third Age "common tongue" of Westron, modelled on Anglo-Saxon (Old English).

When the Edain entered Beleriand early in the fourth century of the First Age, Tolkien portrays them as a wild and proud tribal people who endured terrible trials in their westward migration. The Elves pitied these poor mortals whose span of life was brief and filled with suffering caused by age and disease. And yet, Tolkien's Edain possess a primitive nobility and innate sense of honour that brings them close in spirit to the mortal heroes of Germanic and Norse mythology.

The Edain are comprised of three houses, or dynastic clans, each named after a founding ancestor: the House of Bëor, the House of Haleth and the House of Marach (or Hador). We find similar dynastic clans in Norse and Germanic legend and protohistory, such as the Völsungs (to which Sigurd/Siegfried belongs) and the semi-legendary House of Munsö. In their bravery, strong code of honour and fierce pride, many of the prominent figures in the stories of the Edain – such as Beren, Huor and Tuor – also bear a strong resemblance to the heroes of the Norse and Germanic sagas.

In the Quenya language of the Noldor, these were the Atanatári, or the "Fathers of Men", for the Edain were quick to learn the skills and crafts of the Elves and repaid their mentors with absolute loyalty and supreme acts of self-sacrifice. In these qualities, the Edain are comparable to the heroes of the Norse sagas, who were willing vassals to powerful chieftains and kings in dynastic clans or houses named after their lords. The heroes of these tales were most often the vassals rather than the ruling kings. In the case of the *Völsunga Saga*, the king was Völsung, but the true heroes were his loyal vassals Sigmund and Sigurd, whose counterparts in Tolkien's Middle-earth are to be found among the Edain heroes of the House of Hador.

ARAGORN ELESSAR
JON DAVIS

ARAGORN AND ARTHUR

Aragorn was Tolkien's archetypal hero and future king of the Reunited Kingdom of Arnor and Gondor. English-language readers of *The Lord of the Rings* frequently register a connection between the legendary King Arthur and Aragorn. What is not often apparent, however, is that twelfth- to fourteenth-century Arthurian romances are often based on fifth-century Germanic–Gothic oral epics – epics that now only survive in the myths of their Norse and Icelandic descendants. Tolkien was far more interested in the early Germanic elements of his tales, which link Aragorn with Sigurd the Völsung, the archetypal hero of the Teutonic ring legend.

Although all three heroic warrior kings – Sigurd, Arthur and Aragorn – are clearly similar, the context out of which each arises – in pagan saga, medieval romance and modern fantasy – is very different. The creation of the essentially medieval King Arthur and his court of Camelot, with its Christian ethos, naturally resulted in some reshaping of many of the fiercer aspects of the early pagan tradition. Sigurd the Völsung is a wild warrior who would have been out of place at Arthur's polite, courtly Round Table. Curiously, although Tolkien's Aragorn is essentially a pagan hero, he is often even more upright and ethically driven than the Christian King Arthur.

NOBLE MEN DAVID DAY

When it came to commissioning line-drawing illustrations of races of Mortal Men there was a considerable diversity of styles and approaches: Jon Davis was initially chosen to create line drawings of the noble Men of the Third Age: Dúnedain, the Men of Gondor and the Riders of Rohan.

ARAGORN THE RANGER
JON DAVIS

HELM HAMMERHAND, NINTH KING OF ROHAN
TURNER MOHAN

THÉODEN
ALLAN CURLESS

THÉODEN AND KINGSHIP

The seventeenth king of Rohan and son of Thengel, also known as the King of the Golden Hall. His name is Anglo-Saxon for "lord" or "king", and is related to the Old Norse title for "leader of the people" or "king". In Tolkien's invented language of Rohirric, his name is Tûrac, which once again carries the meaning of "king".

Kingship is important in Middle-earth and seems to be considered part of the natural political order (there are no republics in Middle-earth!). Kings are not like ordinary men and have a quasi-divine quality, as we see especially in the hallowed descent of Aragorn, destined by long lineage to ascend to the throne of Gondor. This is an old tradition in English thought, and Tolkien was a thorough royalist in his sympathies. As William Shakespeare wrote in *Hamlet* (approximately 1599), "divinity doth hedge a king". In Tolkien's world, even when a king goes utterly bad or evil, as with the Witch-king of Angmar, he retains his kingly quality and powers of leadership.

Although a king may become old and weak, like Théoden, his royal gift remains, and, as Tolkien reveals, he can shake off his enfeeblement and resume strength and command. Readers of George MacDonald's classic children's fantasy novel *The Princess and Curdie* (1883) will see a certain debt to the story there of an old king, long kept in a sort of stupor by his wicked servants. With Gandalf's aid, the old king's powers are revived, and he once again becomes "Tûrac Ednew", or "Théoden the Renewed", lord of the Éothéod.

BARBARIANS AND WILD MEN
DAVID DAY

Allan Curless proved to be one of the most innovative and adaptable of illustrators of Tolkien, producing over 40 original drawings that included the heroic Edain of the First Age, and such savage and exotic races of Men as the Balcoth, Easterlings, Wainriders, Corsairs and Beornings. He also created a wonderful depiction of Tolkien's mysterious Woses, the wild woodland people of the Druadan Forest. Tolkien acknowledged that this race was inspired by the medieval tradition of primitive forest dwellers that in turn may have been derived from Greco-Roman legends of satyrs and fauns.

WOSES
ALLAN CURLESS

CORSAIRS
IAN MILLER

WAINRIDERS
ALLAN CURLESS

EASTERLINGS WITH TOTEM
ALLAN CURLESS

EASTERLINGS

Men living in the east of Middle-earth, beyond Mordor and the Sea of Rhun, who from the First Age onward were largely allied with Morgoth and, after his downfall, his successor, Sauron. Easterlings is a translation of the Quenya Romenildi, meaning "East-Men".

The east in Tolkien's writing is both a geographic reality in Middle-earth and an evocation of the history of the European subcontinent, which, in Late Antiquity (AD third–sixth centuries) in particular, saw wave after wave of nomadic peoples, such as the Huns, migrating from the east.

Throughout the history of Tolkien's world, Easterlings in Middle-earth are a constant threat to the kingdoms of the West, just as the Huns and others were a threat to the already crumbling Roman Empire.

In the First Age, the term "Easterling" was applied to Men who came to Beleriand long after the Edain. They were initially known to the Elves as the Swarthy Men on account of their dark hair and skin. One of the great Easterling chieftains is Ulfang the Black, who on his arrival swears allegiance to the Elves of Beleriand, even though he is secretly in league with Morgoth. His betrayal of the Elves in the middle of the Battle of Unnumbered Tears leads to the single most disastrous defeat in the history of Beleriand. This has similarities to the historic betrayal by the Germanic general Arminius (18/17 BC–AD 21), who swore allegiance to Rome but was secretly in league with other German tribes.

In the Battle of Teutoburg Forest in AD 9, Arminius and his allies destroyed three Roman legions in what became known as the Varian Disaster, perhaps the single most costly defeat in Roman history.

Gondor's century of Wainrider invasions (1851–1944 TA), which result in the loss of its eastern territories, owes something to real-world historic accounts of the century-long Roman conflict with the Ostrogoths (East Goths). The Wainriders of Rhûn are a nomadic confederacy of people that travels as an army and nation in vast caravans of wains (wagons) and war chariots. This is certainly comparable to the nomadic Ostrogoths (East Goths), whom one ancient historian described as "an entire nation on the move in great wains".

BEORN

Eponymous chieftain of the Beornings who can take the form of a bear. In human guise, he is a huge, black-bearded man garbed in a coarse wool tunic and armed with a woodsman's axe.

Beorn's appearance in the latter half of the *The Hobbit* establishes the fact that we are now firmly in the heroic world of the Anglo-Saxons, for he appears to be something approaching a twin brother of the epic hero Beowulf. With his pride in his strength, his code of honour, his terrible wrath, and his hospitality, Beorn is Beowulf transposed and brought down in scale. Even his home seems a smaller version of Heorot, the mead-hall of King Hrothgar in the Anglo-Saxon epic poem.

Indeed, Tolkien gives his character a name that, while it sounds and looks a little different from Beowulf's, ends up having much the same meaning, via one of the author's typically convoluted philological puns. Beorn's name means "man" in Old English. However, in its Norse form, it means "bear". Meanwhile, if we look at the Old English name Beowulf, we discover that it literally means "bee-wolf". What, we may wonder, is a bee-wolf? This is typical of the sort of riddle-names that the Anglo-Saxons liked to construct. "What wolf hunts bees – and steals their honey?" The answer is obvious enough: "bee-wolf" is a kenning for a bear: Beowulf and Beorn, then, both mean "bear". Beorn, moreover, is a keeper of bees and a lover of honey. One might say that Beowulf and Beorn are the same men with different names. Or, in their symbolic guise as bee-wolf and bear, they are the same animal in different skins.

Furthermore, Beorn is a "skin-changer", whose people are the likewise shape-shifting Beornings (the "man-bear" people) – Tolkien's fairy-tale version of the historic berserkers (from bear-sark, or "bear-shirt") of the Germanic and Norse peoples. When the berserkers went into battle, they performed rituals and acts of wild frenzy in an attempt to transform into the bears that they believed possessed them. Likewise, in the Battle of the Five Armies, Beorn transforms from fierce warrior to enraged Were-bear, a miraculous event that turns the tide of this critical battle.

THE SEA KINGS OF NÚMENOR

The Second Age is the age of the mighty Sea Kings of Númenor. These are the rulers of the surviving Edain of Beleriand who are given refuge on the island-continent of Andor ("Land of the Gift") in Belegaer, the Sundering Sea, between Middle-earth and the Undying Lands. The island is also known as Elenna-nórë, or "Land of the Star", as it is roughly shaped like a pentagram. As Tolkien undoubtedly knew, this five-pointed star was the sacred symbol of the ancient Greek mystical sect known as the Pythagoreans. This was known as the "Star of Man" because its five points relate to an outstretched body: the head at the top, the arms and hands at the side, and the legs and feet at the bottom.

The first Númenórean king, Elros, and his brother, Elrond, are the twin sons of a mortal man, Eärendil the Mariner, and an immortal Elven maid, Elwing the White. Known as the Peredhil ("Half-elven") because of their mixed blood, they are allowed to choose their race and fate: the mortal world of Men or the immortal world of Elves. Elrond chooses to be immortal and eventually becomes the elven lord of Imladris in Middle-earth. His brother Elros chooses to be mortal (though allowed a lifespan of five centuries) and becomes the founding king of the Númenóreans.

Elros and Elrond have their counterparts in the Greek myth of the twin brothers Castor

LORDS OF THE FIERY DEEP

IAN MILLER

and Pollux. Known as the Dioscuri ("divine twins"), these heroes were the sons of the mortal woman Leda and the immortal god Zeus. In this case, Castor was a mortal man and Pollux an immortal god. When the mortal brother Castor was slain in battle, his immortal brother Pollux was filled with grief because he could never be reunited with his brother, even in the Underworld. Zeus took pity on them and transformed the brothers into the constellation Gemini, the Heavenly Twins.

Tolkien's twins are not reunited and placed among the stars. However, there is a star connection in the figure of Elros and Elrond's father, Eärendil the Mariner. Eärendil was originally an obscure figure in Teutonic myth whom Jacob Grimm associated with the morning star; in Tolkien's tales, Eärendil the Mariner binds the shining Silmaril to his brow and forever rides his flying ship through the firmament, where, in the form of the morning star, he guides all sailors and travellers.

AKALLABÊTH AND ATLANTIS

"The Downfall of Númenor" is Tolkien's reinvention of the ancient Greek Atlantis legend. Tolkien often mentioned that he had "an Atlantis complex", which took the form of a "terrible recurrent dream of the Great Wave, towering up, and coming in ineluctably over the trees and green fields." He appears to have believed that this was some kind of racial memory of the ancient catastrophe of the sinking of Atlantis, and stated on more than one occasion that he had inherited this dream from his parents and had passed it on to his son Michael. In the writing of Akallabêth, however, Tolkien found that he had managed to exorcise this disturbing dream. Evidently, the dream did not reoccur after he dramatized the event in his own tale of the catastrophe.

FASTITOCALON
ALLAN CURLESS

The original legend of Atlantis comes from Plato's dialogues, Timaeus and Critias (both *c.* 360 BC), which include the story of an island kingdom that some nine thousand years before had been home to the mightiest civilization the world had ever known. Atlantis was an island about the size of Spain in the western sea beyond the Pillars of Heracles. Its power extended over all the nations of Europe and the Mediterranean, but the overwhelming pride of these powerful people brought them into conflict with the immortals. Finally, a great cataclysm in the form of a volcanic eruption and a tidal wave resulted in Atlantis sinking beneath the sea. Tolkien used Plato's legend as an outline for Akallabêth. However, Tolkien seems to have been incapable of doing what most authors would have done – writing a straightforward dramatic narrative based on the legend. Typically, he just couldn't help adding little personal touches such as the compilation of three thousand years of detailed history, sociology, geography, linguistics and genealogy.

FASTITOCALON

In Hobbit lore, a vast Turtle-fish that Men believe is an island in the seas. Men build their camps on its back, but when they light their fires, the beast dives beneath the sea drowning all and sundry. A poem about the Fastitocalon is included in Tolkien's *The Adventures of Tom Bombadil* (1968) and is based on medieval legends of the aspidochelone – a giant whale or sea turtle that sailors often mistook for an island and made landfall on its back. An Old English poem about the creature called "The Whal" provided Tolkien with his direct source.

BLACK NÚMENÓREANS

Descendants of the King's Men – supporters of Ar-Pharazôn, last king of the lost island-continent of Númenor – and sworn enemies of the Númenórean Men of Gondor and Arnor. After their settlement in the Númenórean colonies of Middle-earth, the Black Númenóreans – long corrupted by Sauron – continued to worship Morgoth and to flourish even after the downfall of Númenor. Their main centre of power was the city, port, fortress and empire of Umbar.

The portrayal of the Black Númenóreans of Umbar has clear similarities with the Punic inhabitants of the city, port, fortress and empire of Carthage in North Africa. The Carthaginians had a rich, sophisticated culture, but their image in posterity has been largely formed by accounts written by their main rivals for dominance in the western Mediterranean, the Romans, who eventually destroyed Carthage in 146 BC. For the Romans, the Carthaginians were the barbarian "other", whose practices – the worship of demonic gods and, most notoriously, the institution of child sacrifice – contrasted with and validated their own civilized values.

Similarly, in Tolkien's works we typically see the Black Númenóreans through the eyes of the civilized Gondorians: they are lawless, being little better than pirates; they are worshippers of the Lord of the Dark, Morgoth/Melkor (whose name recalls that of Moloch, who is often identified with the Carthaginian chief god Baal Hammon); and they practice human sacrifice to Morgoth using fire, just as the Carthaginians were said to have burned children alive as an offering to Baal.

MEN OF NÚMENOR DAVID DAY

Among the most popular and evocative themes for illustrators of Tolkien is that of the Downfall of Númenor. Like the myth of Atlantis, Númenor is an exemplar of the rise and fall of empires. The fall of Tolkien's Númenor is of the kind that is most often recorded throughout history and myth – where the mighty are seen as growing too proud and self-entitled. Its people, history and spectacular cataclysmic end has held an enduring fascination for illustrators that have been repeatedly imagined over the decades.

CHAOS KNIGHT
IAN MILLER

BEASTS AND DRAGONS

DRAGONS: "NO IDLE FANCY"

" A dragon is no idle fancy", Tolkien once observed. "Whatever may be his origins, in fact or invention, the dragon in legend is a potent creation of men's imagination, richer in significance than his barrow is in gold." In the author's view this truly wonderful monster has such universal appeal that every man in every age may find himself, "caught by the fascination of the worm".

Winged, lizard-like and often fire-breathing beasts found in myths and legends around the world. As the Argentinian author Jorge Luis Borges once explained, dragons are a great mystery: "We are as ignorant of the meaning of the dragon as we are of the meaning of the universe, but there is something in the dragon's image that appeals to the human imagination, and so we find the dragon in quite distant places and times. It is, so to speak, a necessary monster." There is no doubt that Tolkien would have agreed with Borges. Indeed, the appeal of this "necessary monster" was embedded so early and deep in Tolkien's mind that, by the age of seven, "a green great dragon" appeared in his very first original fictional composition. In his landmark lecture and essay "On Fairy-Stories" (lecture 1939; published 1947), Tolkien proudly proclaims this childhood obsession: "I desired dragons with a profound desire. Of course, I in my timid body did not wish to have them in the neighbourhood…but the world that contained even the imagination of Fáfnir [a dragon in Norse mythology] was richer and more beautiful, at whatever the cost of peril."

That childhood obsession eventually inspired his creation of Glaurung, the Father of Dragons, and Ancalagon the Black in *The Silmarillion* and Smaug the Golden in *The Hobbit*, who terrorize the inhabitants of Middle-earth during, respectively, the First and Third Ages. Glaurung was certainly directly inspired by Fáfnir the Dragon slain by Sigurd, the hero of the *Völsunga Saga*. Ancalagon owes his origin in part to the Norse poem *Völuspá*'s account of Ragnarök where a flying dragon, a glowing serpent known as Nidhogg (meaning "malice striker"), appears in that final battle.

DRAGONS
IAN MILLER

THE DRAGON MASTER   DAVID DAY

From the beginning, Ian Miller was our Dragon Master. Ian Miller's dragon cover for *A Tolkien Bestiary* has become a much-admired classic that has been reproduced in over a hundred editions in many languages. His Dragons, Dwarves and Orcs make him the most prominent artist in that book and its updated successor, *The Tolkien Illustrated Encyclopedia*. There is a perennial appeal to Miller's art and he has a unique style and technique that is immediately recognizable. This is in good part due to his trademark pen and ink "Tight-Pen Style" that gives his work a surface that strongly resembles that of a printmaker's cut steel engraving. An artist whose work spans a variety of media, Ian's fans in the film industry include Ralph Bakshi, Michael Crichton and Guillermo del Toro. Del Toro claims to have been inspired as a filmmaker by Ian Miller and acknowledged him as "the foremost illustrator of late 20th century fantasy."

113

GLAURUNG AT THE FIFTH BATTLE
IAN MILLER

GLAURUNG, THE FATHER OF DRAGONS

The first and greatest of the Urulóki, or fire-breathing Dragons, of Middle-earth. This mighty serpent is depicted as being of massive size and strength, and protected by scales of impenetrable iron. His fangs and claws are rapier-sharp, and his great tail can crush the shield-wall of any army. An original creation and villain, Glaurung was – like all of Tolkien's creatures – nonetheless deeply rooted in ancient literature and language.

As his principal inspiration for Glaurung, Tolkien looked to the dragon Fáfnir, the "prince of all dragons" in Norse myth and legend, where he guards a mighty treasure horde and is ultimately slain by the hero Sigurd. Glaurung, however, is perhaps an even more malevolent figure than Fáfnir, because beyond dragon-fire and serpent-strength, Glaurung is cunning (though his intelligence – like all of his species in Norse and Germanic legends – is tempered by the flaws of vanity, gluttony and greed).

The life and death of Glaurung is one of the central tales of *The Silmarillion*, a tale very much inspired by the *Völsunga Saga*. In Tolkien's tale, the Dragon-slayer is Túrin Turambar, who shares many of the characteristics and adventures of Sigurd, the Norse hero of the Icelandic saga. The hero's guile and battle tactics are certainly comparable. For just as Túrin plunges his sword Gurthang into Glaurung's soft underbelly in the slaying of the "Father of Dragons", so Sigurd plunges his sword Gram into Fáfnir's soft underbelly in the slaying of the "prince of all dragons".

GLAURUNG AT THE FIFTH BATTLE
KIP RASMUSSEN

Here, Glaurung battles the forces of Men, Elves and Dwarves, with Azaghal the Dwarf King watching as the beast throws those who have climbed on top of it. Azaghal manages to wound the beast so that it flees the field of battle, but the Dwarf is killed in the process. The weakness he identified is later exploited by Túrin Turambar who slays the monster. Above all, I wanted to depict the immense chaos of the scene which marked the beginning of the end for the forces arrayed against Morgoth.

THE ARMIES OF MORGOTH
MAURO MAZZARA

ANCALAGON THE BLACK

The first and greatest of the vast legion of Winged Fire Drakes that Morgoth releases from the deep dungeons of Angband in the last battle of the War of Wrath at the end of the First Age. The attack of Ancalagon (meaning "rushing jaws") in that last Great Battle has a precedent in the account of the great Norse battle of Ragnarök found in the Old Norse poem *Völuspá* (part of the *Poetic Edda*) where "the flying dragon, glowing serpent" known as Nidhogg (meaning "malice striker") emerges from the underworld, Niflheim. Like Nidhogg, the ravening majesty that is Ancalagon unleashes a terrible withering fire down from the heavens.

In the Prose Edda's account of Ragnarök, we have another dragon-like monster, Jörmungandr, the World-Serpent, who rises up with the giants to do battle with the gods, and bring about the destruction of the Nine Worlds. In this version of Ragnarök, the god Thor appears in his flying chariot and, armed with the thunderbolt hammer Mjölnir, slays Jörmungandr. In Tolkien's Great Battle, the hero Eärendil appears in his flying ship Vingilótë and, armed with a Silmaril, slays Ancalagon.

YOUNG GUNS DAVID DAY

With the publishers' decision to create a multi-volume reference library for a new generation of my readers in 2013, it was an obvious requirement to recruit a new generation of talented illustrators. Kip Rasmussen and Mauro Mazzara are two talented artists and rising stars in the firmament of fantasy illustrators. Kip and Mauro both took on the formidable challenge of illustrating heroic encounters between dragons and dragon-slayers.

Kip has a particular appreciation for the poetic language and archaic tone of Tolkien's writing in *The Silmarillion*, and consequently responded as an artist by creating haunting and evocative scenes of great beauty and power. This is especially true of his many hugely powerful and atmospheric illustrations of battles with dragons. Of the many that featured in *The Heroes of Tolkien* and *The Dark Powers of Tolkien*, certainly among the most remarkable was his fantastic portrayal of the battle between Glaurung the Father of Dragons and Azaghal the Dwarf king of Belegost.

Mauro created his own spectacular scenario in *The Armies of Morgoth*, depicting the armies of Elves and Men of Beleriand finding themselves confronted by legions of Orcs backed by the unstoppable terror of a fire-breathing Dragon with a bodyguard of Balrog demons in the War of Wrath. Mauro has proved to be a gifted artist with a flamboyant and dramatic style that blends in with a deep knowledge of history that is essential to successfully illustrating Tolkien's world. This has proved to be especially important in his works created for *The Battles of Tolkien*, *The Heroes of Tolkien* and *The Dark Powers of Tolkien* where each of these are concerned with the historic, literary and cultural inspiration behind Tolkien's writing.

SMAUG VS. BARD THE BOWMAN
KIP RASMUSSEN

THE PERFECT FAIRY-TALE DRAGON

Smaug was inspired by the nameless dragon portrayed in the Anglo-Saxon epic poem *Beowulf*. Tolkien was one who searched for "dragons, real dragons, essential both to the machinery and the ideas of a poem or tale." He found elements of his Dragons in Germanic literature and mythology, but also very specifically in *Beowulf*, a poem that provided both the monster and much of the plot outline for his fairy-tale novel, *The Hobbit*.

The Hobbit takes its basic plotline from *Beowulf* and his fatal encounter with a dragon. In that ancient poem, a thief enters the dragon's lair and steals a gold cup. In Tolkien's tale the thief is the Hobbit, Bilbo Baggins. And in both tales, the theft of a gold cup awakens a sleeping dragon that emerges from its lair to lay waste to a nearby kingdom. *The Hobbit* is essentially the *Beowulf* dragon story told from the thief's point of view. There is, however, one problem with *Beowulf*'s dragon. It is more the terrifying embodiment of an evil curse than an individual villain that happens to be a dragon.

All characters in a really good fairy-tale adventure must offer the reader something of a close-up, intimate feeling. This is true of all of an adventure's characters, even – or especially – the bad ones. The trouble with the *Beowulf* dragon is that the closer you come, the more it recedes. You cannot gain a hold on it. In fact, the monster is not even given a name. For Tolkien, this was a cardinal sin. Within the spheres of Middle-earth names are the primary factors in all life forms and his chief motivation in the creation of all things. It may be suggested that Tolkien began to feel like the maiden in "Rumpelstiltskin" whose fate depended on discovering the creature's true name. With this end in mind, and a philological search through a series of Old English and prehistoric German words he arrived at the name "Smaug".

So Tolkien decided "Smaug the Golden", "Smaug the Magnificent" and "Lord Smaug the Impenetrable" would be the names of the greatest Dragon of the Third Age. Not simply a Cold-drake like those haunting the Dwarf mansions of the Grey Mountains, Smaug was to be a full-fledged golden-red Fire-drake.

Smaug had vast wings like a bat and a coat of impenetrable iron scales. Far better than a large but nameless lizard like *Beowulf*'s monster. The name "Smaug the Greatest of Calamities" carried the collective meaning of its composite parts in Old English: penetrating, inquiring, burrowing, worming into and creeping through. These were all useful clues to a really slippery, intelligent and nasty villain. Then, too, came an appropriate – if accidental – pun on smog, which insinuates its way through a distinctive whiff of brimstone.

To all the sinister qualities gained by way of the naming of Smaug, Tolkien added a multitude of aspects in legendary dragons dating back to the ancient Greek Python of Delphi as a fierce guardian of treasure: a great serpent; a keeper of arcane knowledge; a monster with an inquiring mind, a terrifying glance and a mesmerizing voice. It is certain that from this hoard of dragon lore, Smaug the Worm of Dread inherited its laser eyes, brilliant intellect, mesmerizing spells and a few of its other more terrifying qualities.

And yet, as Tolkien famously wrote in his lecture and essay "On Fairy-Stories": "The dragon had the trade-mark of Faerie written plain upon him." This is perhaps why his dragons either appear in the ancient mythic world of Elves in *The Silmarillion* or the children's fairy-tale world of Hobbits in *The Hobbit*, but not in the epic high romance world of mortal Men in *The Lord of the Rings*.

THE DEATH OF SMAUG DAVID DAY

The death of Smaug the Dragon is certainly one of the most dramatic moments in Tolkien's *The Hobbit*. It is also one of the most popular and challenging events for an artist to attempt to illustrate. Kip Rasmussen's painting of Bard the Bowman's black arrow piercing the soft underbelly of Smaug the Golden Dragon is a stunning and original vision of that critical turning point in Tolkien's novel.

It is interesting to compare Kip's vision with that of the British artist Allan Curless, who was commissioned to re-create exactly that same event 39 years earlier. Allan Curless was one of the major contributors to *A Tolkien Bestiary*, contributing over 40 drawings and watercolours to the book. He was one of the most versatile of illustrators creating haunting and memorable images, such as those of the Witch-king and the Nazgûl Ringwraiths mounted on phantom horses and upon Winged Beasts. But he also produced numerous drawings of a multitude of birds, beasts, flora and fauna of Middle-earth. Sadly, Allan passed away too soon in 1997. It would perhaps have pleased him to see his *Smaug* still providing pleasure to readers of Tolkien. For although *Smaug* first appeared in *A Tolkien Bestiary* in 1979, it was republished in *The Tolkien Illustrated Encyclopedia* in 1992 and posthumously proved to be a favourite cover design for many American and foreign language editions of *The World of Tolkien* since 2002.

SMAUG
ALLAN CURLESS

SCATHA THE WORM

After the near-obliteration of the Dragons of Middle-earth at the end of the First Age in the last Great Battle of the War of Wrath, it is not until the twentieth century of the Third Age that the histories of Middle-earth speak again of dragons. These monsters are akin to the dragons found in the Middle High German heroic epics of Wolfdietrich and Ortnit. Like the dragons of the mountains of Lombardy who appear in these thirteenth-century tales, the monsters who make their presence known in the Grey Mountains of Middle-earth in the Third Age are Cold-drakes: a somewhat less formidable breed of dragon than either the Fire-drakes or the Winged Fire-drakes of the First Age. And yet, even lacking the power of fire or flight, the great strength of these serpents, with their fangs, claws and armour of iron scales, made them a terror of their times.

The mightiest of the Cold-drakes of the Grey Mountains who slaughtered Dwarves and Men and took possession of a great treasure hoard is Scatha the Worm. Appropriately enough, Scatha's name was derived from an Anglo-Saxon word meaning "Assassin". Scatha's end at the hand of Fram the Éothéod Dragon-slayer was comparable to that of the Cold-drake that died at the hand of Wolfdietrich, the Langobard Dragon-slayer. Meanwhile, the slaying of Dain I, king of the Dwarves, by the Cold-drakes of the Grey Mountains is mirrored in the slaying of Ortnit, king of the Langobards, by Cold-drakes in the mountains of Lombardy.

The Langobards were one of the many powerful German tribes who lived on the eastern European borderlands of the Roman Empire. These warrior people swept into northern Italy where they settled and gave their name to the region today called Lombardy. Described by Latin historians as the supreme horsemen of the German peoples, the Langobards were Tolkien's models for the Éothéod and their heirs the Rohirrim (the Horsemen of Rohan). Also, curiously enough, the tribal name "Langobards" translates directly into English as "Longbeards", the same name Tolkien gave to the Dwarves of Durin's Line, and to Dain I, the Longbeard king of the Grey Mountains.

Ortnit, the eponymous hero of the Langobard epic poem, was the son of Alberich, the legendary dwarf king of the Italian Alps. Just as Dain I's kingdom in the Grey Mountains was terrorized by Cold-drakes, so Ortnit's kingdom was terrorized by Cold-drakes in the Lombard Mountains.

READ AND REACT   IAN MILLER

Finding a style for *A Tolkien Bestiary* drawings evolved in a very freeflow fashion. I read the text and reacted. Nobody dictated form or feel other than providing the page configurations, showing the illustration areas I was required to fill. They just pressed the button and let me go. Line drawings of Dragons first, then Ents, the Balrog, Dwarves and Barrow-wights. Orcs, elephants, spiders and other characters followed, interspersed with a number of coloured double pages.

BALROG OF ANGBAND
IAN MILLER

BALROGS OF ANGBAND

Known as the Valaraukar or "Cruel Demons" in Quenya, these mighty Maiar fire spirits are among the most terrifying of Morgoth's servants in the War of the Jewels. More commonly known to the Sindar of Beleriand as Balrogs, or "Demons of Might", they take the form of man-shaped giants shrouded in darkness, with manes of fire, eyes that glow like burning coals, and nostrils that breathe flame. Balrogs wield many-thonged whips of fire in battle, in combination with a mace, axe or flaming sword.

Visually, the Balrogs, while male, are comparable to the demonic Erinyes (Furies) of Greek mythology, female chthonic deities and avenging spirits – called Alecto, Tisiphone and Megaera – who emerged from the pits of the Underworld to pursue those guilty of crime. Furies were variously described as having snakes for hair, coal-black bodies, bats' wings, and blood-red eyes. They attacked their victims with blazing torches and many-thonged brass-studded whips.

There can be little doubt, however, that Tolkien's primary source for the Balrogs was the fire giants of Muspelheim, the mythical Norse "region of fire". The giant inhabitants of Muspelheim were demonic fire spirits who – once released – were as unstoppable as the volcanic lava floes that were so familiar to the Norsemen of Iceland.

There is also a link with Tolkien's Anglo-Saxon studies. Since Jc's publication of Tolkien's notes on the Old English poem Exodus, several scholars have linked this text with his invention of the Balrogs. In these notes, Tolkien took issue with the usual modern translation of the Exodus's "Sigelwara land" as the land of the Ethiopians. Tolkien believed that Sigelwara was a scribal error for sigel-hearwa, the land of "sun-soot", and was instead a reference to Muspelheim. The Sigelwara therefore were the fire giants – in Tolkien's own words, "rather the sons of Músspel…than of Ham [the biblical ancestor of the Ethiopians], the ancestors of the Silhearwan with red-hot eyes that emitted sparks, with faces as black as soot".

BALROGS   DAVID DAY

It is instructive to view how the fantastically hellish fire demon that is J R R Tolkien's Balrog has been portrayed over the decades. The first illustration of the Balrog of Angband was drawn by Ian Miller in 1979 for *A Tolkien Bestiary*. The second, of the Balrog of Moria, was created by Sam Hadley for *The World of Tolkien* in 2002; while the third was envisioned by Mauro Mazzara in 2016 for *The Battles of Tolkien*.

It is interesting to note how wildly different these interpretations of the monsters are, despite each being drawn from exactly the same Tolkien description. It is curious how Tolkien's masterful description can evoke horror in all who read it, but no one can really agree on what exactly has been described. Curiously enough, there has been a long-running dispute among hardcore Tolkien fans over the nature and physical attributes of the Balrog. No one, it seems, can come to an agreement on whether or not Balrogs have wings.

THREE BALROGS   DAVID DAY

To many artists – Ian Miller among them – this lack of agreement about even the most basic features of the Balrog is a boon that allows an artistic licence without limits. All three of these illustrators have taken advantage of this and created unique visions of this monster. In Ian Miller's rendering we have a fire spirit drawn in his distinctive close-hatched pen and ink style that seems to be reminiscent of the engravings of Albrecht Durer. Although, in knowing Ian Miller's deep interest in Japanese martial arts, it is not difficult to see something of the Samurai warlord in his Balrog.

Sam Hadley is a highly adaptable commercial artist who has produced work from book covers to billboards and video games to hand painted murals. He has a wide range of styles from photo-realistic airbrushing to more traditional painting and drawing. In 2002, he brought a heavy metal version of the Balrog into its famous confrontation with Gandalf in the Battle of the Bridge of Khazad-dûm.

Mauro Mazzara provides a very different version of the Balrog's battle with Gandalf on the Bridge of Khazad-dûm. His battle with the Balrog is an operatic drama on a spectacular scale in a sword and sorcery world. Mazzara claims the celebrated Tolkien illustrator John Howe as a mentor who inspired him as an artist. It is also quite possible to see something of one of John Howe's mentors – the great sword and sorcery artist Frank Frazetta – as perhaps indirectly influencing Mauro's art.

A HOMAGE   MAURO MAZZARA

John Howe has been one of my biggest inspirations growing up. His unforgettable illustrations are simply sublime. *Gandalf vs. the Balrog* is a homage to the amazing work he has been doing. Sometimes the same few words lead the imagination of us all in the very same direction. Sometimes very short descriptions from Tolkien give a lot of space to the imagination. I guess this is the case of the battle between Gandalf and the Balrog – that amazing battle between light and darkness. Red against blue. Evil against good.

GANDALF VS. THE BALROG
MAURO MAZZARA

WARGS

A breed of demonic wolf in Middle-earth. From the First Age to the Third Age, Wargs work in alliance with Goblins and Orcs, most obviously as steeds for the Orc Wolf-riders in battles and as scouts for Sauron or Saruman. As Aragorn the Ranger succinctly observes in *The Lord of the Rings*: "Where the warg howls, there also the orc prowls." The Wargs of Middle-earth are not only more fierce and frightening than ordinary wolves, but there is something supernatural in their nature that makes them more akin to werewolves. Just how sentient and communicative Wargs are is not made clear, though Tolkien does speak of the "dreadful language of the Wargs".

Tolkien derived the word "Warg" from the Anglo-Saxon warg or wearg, meaning "strangler" or "choker" but also "outlaw" or "criminal". The Wargs' close association with the forces of Sauron the Necromancer underlines the latter's connections with the Norse god Odin who was accompanied by two wolves, Geri and Freki, both names meaning "greedy".

WOLVES

The belief in lycanthropy – of humans who intermittently change into wolves, often at full moon – is part of the folklore and mythology of every civilization that interacts (or has once interacted) with wolves. Wolves and werewolves also loom large in Tolkien's legendarium.

WARGS
MAURO MAZZARA

DRAUGLUIN

The Father of Werewolves – sire of all those "creatures that walk in wolf-shape" upon Middle-earth. His name in Sindarin means "Blue Wolf", in reference to the colour of his coat. Draugluin was bred by Morgoth or else was a corrupted Maia. He haunts the dungeons within the fortress of Tol-in-Gaurhoth ("Isle of Werewolves") in Beleriand and plays a key role in the Quest for the Silmaril, where he is slain by Huan, the Hound of the Valar.

As a "hellhound" guardian, Draugluin shares many similarities with Carcharoth, whom he sires, and hence with other hellhounds such as Cerberus in Greek mythology and Garm in Norse mythology. As a demonic spirit, his creation may owe something to the darker aspects of both Odin and Zeus, who were both associated with wolves and werewolves.

Although not prominent in the histories of the Second and Third Ages of Middle-earth, Draugluin's descendants may have been present among the Wolves and Wargs that allied themselves with Orcs, Trolls, Wraiths and other dark forces.

CARCHAROTH

"Red Maw", the greatest Wolf to appear in Middle-earth – sired by Draugluin, and reared on living flesh by the hand of Morgoth, Carcharoth is the unsleeping guardian at the gates of the subterranean kingdom of Angband. Carcharoth is comparable to guardians of the gates in other mythological underworlds, such as the Norse Garm, the gigantic hound guardian of Helheim, and the Greek Cerberus, the monstrous three-headed hound that was the unsleeping guardian at the gates of Hades.

THE WITCH-KING OF ANGMAR
ALLAN CURLESS

NAZGÛL

The name in the Black Speech of the Orcs for the Ringwraiths, the terrible phantom nine Black Riders who are the greatest servants of Sauron the Ring Lord through much of the Second and Third Ages. The Nazgûl were once kings and sorcerers, but Sauron corrupted them using the power of the Nine Rings of Mortal Men.

In his creation of the malignant and terrifying Ringwraiths, Tolkien taps into rich lodes of mythology and legend. The wraith is a phantom or spectre, either a manifestation of a living being or the ghost of a dead person. In English, "wraith" is a relatively recent word, first noted around 1513, but the notion it conveys is of vastly greater antiquity than the English language. For humans, the primal mysteries are birth and death, and of the two, death is much harder to comprehend. Fear of the dead is a powerful force in all cultures, based on the belief that if the dead were to return, it almost invariably results in evil and disaster.

The Nazgûl have immense powers over the mind and will of their foes, but they themselves are Sauron's slaves in their every action, and they barely exist except as terrifying phantoms, acting as lethal extensions of the Ring Lord's eternal lust for power and his desire to enslave all life. The Nine Rings of Mortal Men give the Nazgûl the power to preserve their "undead" forms as terrifying wraiths for thousands of years. Certain aspects of Tolkien's Nazgûl are shared with the zombie, a mindless reanimated corpse set in motion by a sorcerer. However, in the Nazgûl, Tolkien created beings far more potent and malevolent. Not only are they possessed by the will of Sauron but even before they were seduced as the Dark Lord's thralls these were sorcerers and kings of great power among the Easterlings of Rhûn, the Southrons of Harad and the mighty Men of Númenor.

We should not overlook the fact that the Nazgûl are nine in number. It is a mystic number in both white and black magic of many nations, from the proverbial nine lives of the cat to Pythagorean numerology in which nine is assigned as the number of the tyrant. In Norse mythology, nine is by far the most significant number, from the Nine Worlds of its cosmology to the nine nights Odin the Hanged God suffered on the World Tree. The greatest Viking religious ceremonies at Uppsala lasted nine days on every ninth year. Nine is the last of the series of single numbers, and, as such, in Norse mythology and others, it is seen as symbolizing both death and rebirth. And, in Tolkien's world, the Nine Rings are Sauron's payment for the purchase of those nine eternally damned souls who become the nine Nazgûl.

NAZGÛL ON WINGED BEASTS
ALLAN CURLESS

PTEROSAURS

Name given to extinct flying reptiles that existed some 228 to 66 million years ago. The word comes from the Greek pterosaurus, meaning "winged lizard".

When asked about the origin of the winged beasts that served as the horrific airborne mounts of the Ringwraiths, Tolkien acknowledged that they resembled pterosaurs and that, on Middle-earth, they might even be survivors from an older geological age. This seems to have been already hinted at in *The Lord of the Rings* where the fearsome steeds of the Nazgûl are nameless, though variously described by Tolkien as Fell Beasts, Hell-hawks and Nazgúl-birds: "if bird, then greater than all other birds, and it was naked, and neither quill nor feather did it bear, and its vast pinions were as webs of hide between horned fingers; and it stank. A creature of an older world maybe it was."

HORSEMEN OF THE APOCALYPSE

Four horsemen in the biblical Book of Revelation (6:1–8), harbingers of an age of destruction and catastrophe. Each horseman was thought to symbolize a scourge: Pestilence, War, Famine and Death. Although Four Horsemen of the Apocalypse are described, their terrifying collective impact is comparable to the nine mounted Ringwraiths, or Nazgûl, of Middle-earth, who are the ghastly servants of Sauron the Ring Lord. One traditional Christian reading of the Four Horsemen saw in them a prophecy of the eventual decline and fall of the Roman Empire. And in the nine Ringwraiths, too, we see a foreshadowing of the Pestilence, War, Famine and Death that threaten to come down upon the inhabitants on the kingdom of Gondor and the other lands of Middle-earth.

RINGWRAITHS
VICTOR AMBRUS

THE BLACK RIDERS

Name given to the Nazgûl when Sauron sends them out on horseback to track down the Ring and its keeper, "Baggins". They are the first truly evil entities to appear in *The Lord of the Rings*, in the green and pleasant Hobbit land of the Shire. The identity of these cloaked and hooded horsemen is not immediately revealed, but eventually they are proved to be the Ringwraiths. It is only later, through the eyes of the Ring-bearer Frodo Baggins, that the reader is given a glance of the Nazgûl as they appear to the Necromancer and those who inhabit the wraith-world. After slipping the One Ring on his finger, the Hobbit is suddenly able to see in the phantom shapes of the Ringwraiths their terrible white faces, grey hair, long grey robes and "helms of silver".

In some ways, the Black Riders are not unlike the phantom horsemen in the English poet John Keats's ballad "La Belle Dame Sans Merci" (1819): a ghostly host of men seduced and enslaved by the "beautiful lady without mercy" of the title, and described as "Pale kings and princes, too, / Pale warriors, death-pale were they all." The "palely loitering" kings and sorcerers who make up the Nazgûl have been similarly seduced, though not by the charms of a beautiful enchantress, but by Sauron and their overweening desire for power and a near-eternal life.

THE BLACK RIDERS
ALLAN CURLESS

PUCKERED APPLES   IAN MILLER

Drawing things from the slough is far more fun, and offers a good deal more licence in its interpretation than nice things. How can you overdo a wart or the twist of an Orc's pig iron boot, or use the wrong hue of dung brown. "Freedom in filth, and all thing paludal" screamed the turtle. The idea of drawing a beautiful Elf maiden would have sent me running – still does in fact – and happily no one has ever asked me to.

    With a muted range of colours to hand, the work goes on. Better a puckered apple than rose petal lips says I?

GOBLINS

In European folklore, goblins are grotesque, devil-like creatures akin to imps and kobolds, usually but not always malevolent, or at least mischievous. In Tolkien's legendarium, they appear in *The Hobbit*, in the Goblins and the Great Goblin of Goblin Town, used as a synonym for the evil race of Orcs.

Tolkien's *The Hobbit* and its Goblins owe a debt of inspiration to the Scottish writer George MacDonald (1824–1905) and his 1872 novel *The Princess and the Goblin*, as Tolkien explicitly acknowledged in a letter. A little MacDonald song, included in his novel, begins: "Once there was a Goblin / Living in a hole…". This is very close to Tolkien's opening line in *The Hobbit*: "In a hole in the ground there lived a hobbit."

In *The Hobbit* the narrator warns the reader that the Misty Mountains are made perilous by hordes of "goblins, hobgoblins and orcs of the worst description." Each of these names is a synonym for the other, or very nearly, as Tolkien himself explained in the preface to his novel: "Orc is not an English word. It occurs in one or two places [in *The Hobbit*] but is usually translated goblin (or hobgoblin for the larger kinds)." Orcs, of course, in Middle-earth, are the evil foot soldiers of the Dark Lords Morgoth and Sauron. However, the publishing history of Tolkien novels ensured that readers would first encounter them under the Goblin name.

The Hobbit was written decades after most of *The Silmarillion* was conceived, but with his young audience in mind Tolkien needed to somewhat mute the evil nature of his cannibalistic Orcs, adopting instead the rather more mischievous comic nature of the fairy-tale goblins found in MacDonald. However, readers who progress from *The Hobbit* to the high romance of *The Lord of the Rings* and the heroic age of *The Silmarillion* soon discover that Tolkien no longer portrays Goblins simply as comic grotesques, but as the seriously irredeemably evil race of Middle-earth in thrall to the Dark Lord.

Tolkien also speaks of his borrowing from "the Goblin tradition", so one must also acknowledge the international nature of these creatures. His Goblins share many aspects with Germanic, Nordic and British traditions, with kobolds, bogies, knockers, bugbears, red caps, demons, imps, sprites and gremlins, as well as with beings from the folk traditions of Asia, such as the Malayan Toyol or Cambodian Cohen Kroh, evil, twisted spirits animating the bodies of murdered children or fetuses.

THE HORDE
MAURO MAZZARA

ORCS   IAN MILLER

Given the available histories and descriptions, the Orcs and Uruk-hai were not overly difficult to visualise or illustrate. As to the weapons and armour they used, and mindful of their torturous and corrupted genesis, I decided on a cruder, blight-edged variation, on the much finer wrought Dwarf and Dunlending armour and weapons than I presented in other *A Tolkien Bestiary* pictures.

THE HORDE — MAURO MAZZARA

"Horde". This is the word I had in my mind all the time. The most bizarre horde I could create, that goes from the first line to the horizon. Evil, evil, evil creatures everywhere. There's no hope against it. Or maybe there is? "At sunrise, look to the East", Gandalf says.

I wanted to show that – just like humans – goblins, hobgoblins and Orcs are different from one another. With the colours I tried to merge everything all together, but each being has its own character and features. Each one has a story and history that took them to that moment on the battlefield. Scars. Fungus. Infections. Body shape. Every detail tells that story. In the few moments before the battle, the most stupid ones don't even understand why they are there. The most evil can't wait to slay humans. The smallest one probably knows they are just "cannon fodder"…or maybe they are way too stupid as well?

ORCS

The evil, goblin-like soldiers of the Dark Lords Morgoth and Sauron in Middle-earth. Tolkien's Orcs originate in the early First Age when Melkor captures many of the newly awoken race of Elves, takes them down into his fortress dungeons of Utumno (and later Angband). There, he tortures and transforms them into a race of slaves and soldiers who are as loathsome as the Elves are fair. The Orcs are hideous, stunted and muscular with yellow fangs, blackened faces and red slits for eyes.

Tolkien's Orcs appear, like so many of his races, to have multiple sources of inspiration. In *Beowulf*, mention is made of orcneas (ironically in juxtaposition with ylfe – elves) as being among the "evil broods". The word perhaps suggests "walking corpses", like living dead, or zombies, the component word orc perhaps deriving from the Latin word Orcus, an Etruscan and Roman god of the underworld and for the underworld itself. However, in a letter, Tolkien wrote that he himself doubted this derivation. The word "orc" also appears in sixteenth-century English to mean a devouring monster, while the man-eating ogres of fairy tales are another, related breed.

So much for the etymological inspirations. The concept and nature of Orcs, as demonic underlings programmed to do the bidding of their evil masters, has resonance with numerous myths and tales from around the world. Such demons are prominent, for example, in the Old Testament where demons are considered innumerable (and often invisible), preferring to live in isolated, unclean places such as deserts and ruins, and greatly to be feared, especially at night. In all of Tolkien's descriptions of Orcs, they, too, create a sense of vast anonymous numbers and are likened to innumerable swarms or devastating black waves. They come pouring out of caverns with impersonal, insect-like inexorability and are often compared by the author to flies or ants.

ORCS

IAN MILLER

URUK-HAI
MAURO MAZZARA

URUKS AND THE HUNS

Uruks, or Uruk-hai, are a swarthy-skinned and lynx-eyed warrior race that Sauron breeds and releases in the twenty-fifth century of the Third Age, as a new and more powerful breed of Orkish soldiery. They may have resulted from an interbreeding of Orcs and Men.

It has been suggested that these larger and more ferocious forms of Orcs may in part have been inspired by Tolkien's reading of the sixth-century Eastern Roman historian Jordanes and his xenophobic description of the "scarcely human" Huns. Sauron's Uruks are Orkish in appearance and manner, but the size of Men and could endure and remain strong in sunlight. Jordanes' description of the soldiery of the Hunnic leader Attila, the Scourge of God, might easily have been applied to Sauron's Uruks: "Their swarthy aspect is fearful, and they have pin-holes rather than eyes...Broad-shouldered, ready to use a bow and arrow. Though they live in the form of Men, they have the cruelty of wild beasts."

Like the Huns against the Romans, the Uruk-hai come forth in great numbers against the Men of Gondor. They lay waste to their capital, Osgiliath, and for the next five centuries of the Third Age, the Uruks fight in Sauron's alliance alongside lesser Orcs, Trolls, Easterlings and Southrons.

URUK-HAI
IAN MILLER

TROLLS

Huge humanoid monsters that can be discovered in the folklore and legends in every region of the world. They leave their footprints all over the landscape, move mountains and change the course of rivers. In many folktales, large standing stones are believed to be Trolls that have been turned to stone after being exposed to sunlight. They appear to prefer living in mountain caverns or dark forest caves from which they emerge to prey on lost children and unwary travellers.

The Trolls of Middle-earth draw on two major troll traditions. One we might loosely call "Scandinavian", and the other "fairy tale". Tolkien's portrayal of Trolls in *The Hobbit* owes a great deal to the trolls of fairy tale where they are most often dull-witted creatures who are simply content with random, if brutal, acts of mayhem and mischief. The three Trolls encountered by Bilbo Baggins and Thorin and Company (Bert, Tom and William Huggins) are very much of the comic fairy-tale variety (rather like overgrown louts), and the Wizard Gandalf's outwitting of the Trolls by keeping them arguing until the sun rises, and thereby turning them to stone, is clearly based on the Brothers Grimm tale "The Brave Little Tailor".

Elsewhere in the legendarium, however, Tolkien's Trolls are an altogether more serious matter. While they are still lumbering, vicious and dull-witted, as tools in the hands of Morgoth in the First Age or Sauron in the Second and Third, they are extremely dangerous, by force of their massive strength alone. A Hill-troll kills Aragorn's grandfather, Arador; Cave-trolls attack the Fellowship of the Ring in Moria; and Mountain-trolls lead the assault on the gates of Minas Tirith. These Trolls, it seems, are largely inspired by Norse myths of the *jötnar*, a word often misleadingly translated as "giants" but which in fact were manifestations of the fierce powers of nature, of mountain, forest and blistering cold. It's worth noting, too, that in the Anglo-Saxon epic *Beowulf*, the monster Grendel is described as a "water-haunting Troll".

NOT TOO BIG, NOR TOO SMALL
LIDIA POSTMA

You have to understand a Hobbit to be able to depict him, not become one. Because Hobbits cannot depict themselves – that would diminish them. To each other, of course, they are full-sized. Anything other is too big or too small.

MORGOTH ENSNARED BY UNGOLIANT
KIP RASMUSSEN

UNGOLIANT AND SPIDERS

A primordial monster in *The Silmarillion* that takes the shape of a gigantic female spider. Sometimes called the "Gloomweaver", Tolkien's monster weaves a web of darkness and horror from a substance that Tolkien calls the "Unlight of Ungoliant".

Ungoliant's exact origins in terms of Tolkien's cosmology are left obscure in his writings. We are told that she is from "before the world", which only serves to heighten the black vastness of her evil. Tolkien's arachnophobic characterization of his Great Spiders is consistent with the portrayal of India's eight-limbed Kali the Black One, the "Destroyer of the World", who dances on the slaughtered body of her lover. However, this is not in keeping with most of the world's mythologies. Despite the formidable reputation of the black widow, the fact remains that only thirty out of the forty-three thousand spider species in existence are capable of seriously harming humans.

In the ancient Mediterranean world, from Egypt to Babylon, Greece and Rome, tales equate the spider with spinning and weaving, skills essential to all civilizations. Ultimately, spiders are personified as the Fates who spin the destinies of men and gods, the direct antithesis of Ungoliant and Shelob. In these cultures spiders are deities of creation. In Africa and the West Indies we have widespread variations on Anansi, the Ashanti spider god who is the creator god and a trickster in many folk tales. He is also transformed into Aunt Nancy in many children's "spider tales", which are essentially allegorical stories and moral lessons. The Hopi and Navaho have creation myths of the wise Spider Mother or Grandmother who weaves the world into existence. Other myths among North and South American (and some Oceanic) Indigenous peoples portray the spider god as a trickster and creator who weaves constellations of stars or the entire universe into existence.

In Eastern Painted Scrolls, we find a "Master of Non-Being", an entity similar to Ungoliant, but in a male form that actually resembles Morgoth, the Dark Lord. Indeed, in this huge "Master of Non-Being", the identity of Morgoth and Ungoliant merge as one in this living form of darkness. The Master is a massive scorched black demon described as a "Black Man, as tall as a spear…the Master of Non-Existence, of instability, of murder and destruction." And just as Ungoliant and Morgoth together extinguish the sacred Trees of Light in the Undying Lands, the Eastern Master of Non-Being "made the sun and the moon die and assigned demons to the planets and harmed the stars."

The tale of Ungoliant provides a philosophical or theological account of the nature of evil. In Tolkien's Roman Catholic Christian view – rooted in the theology of Saint Augustine of Hippo (AD 354–430) – evil is nothing but the absence of good. In a letter, Tolkien explained: "In my story I do not deal in Absolute Evil. I do not think there is such a thing, since that is Zero."

In the end, in her insatiable hunger Ungoliant devours herself. Ungoliant and Morgoth are destined to a self-devouring annihilation, a return to the Void and the nothingness of "Non-Being".

THE WOUNDING OF SHELOB
LIDIA POSTMA

SHELOB THE GREAT SPIDER

The "last child" of the gargantuan Ungoliant the Mother of All Spiders of the First Age, in *The Lord of the Rings*. In the Second and Third Age, Shelob the Great and her offspring "lesser broods, bastards of [her] miserable mates" lived in the mountains of Mordor and forest of the Mirkwood. Ungoliant and Shelob's portrayals as monsters capable of paralyzing and killing their prey, and as females who in the act of mating cannibalize their male partners, have some valid basis in zoology. This is in largely due to the appropriately named real world black widow spiders, which have toxic venom that paralyzes or kills its prey, and which do have the deeply unpleasant habit of occasionally devouring their much smaller male partners while in the act of mating.

Although Shelob (an Old English construct meaning "She-Spider") did not reach the majestic proportions of Ungoliant, she was the greatest and largest Spider of the Second and Third Age. In what could be described in biological terms as successive degeneration, Shelob, the guardian of Cirith Ungol, was about as big as a ploughhorse, while her offspring the Spiders of the Mirkwood in *The Hobbit* were "very much smaller and less intelligent".

The Hobbits' descent into Shelob's Lair has been described as comparable to the descent into the Underworld in Virgil's *Aeneid*. Gollum serves as Frodo and Sam's guide, just as the Sibyl serves as Aeneas' guide. Sam uses the Phial of Galadriel to overcome Shelob and escape, while a golden bough and a drugged cake are used to bypass Charon the Ferryman and Cerberus the three-headed Hell Hound. Tales of descent into the underworld are most often attempts by heroes to return loved ones to the world of the living. Aeneas cannot bring his father back to life, but Sam succeeds in reviving Frodo after Shelob's poison places him in a state resembling death.

Just as Ungoliant was the counterpart of Morgoth the Dark Lord, so Shelob was the counterpart of Sauron the Dark Lord. Neither were true spiders, but evil entities in spider form that are something akin to the medieval portrayal of the deadly sins of lust, envy, sloth, wrath, pride, gluttony and greed. These monsters served in both Dark Lords' plans up to a point. However, ultimately, neither accepted a master. Ungoliant turned upon Morgoth, while Shelob proved equally ungovernable and served "none but herself."

SMÉAGOL/GOLLUM

Sméagol is the Westron translation of the original Hobbitish name Trahald for the cannibalistic ogre that became known as Gollum. Bilbo Baggins first encountered this repellent creature in the caverns beneath Goblin Town in *The Hobbit*. In the beginning, Sméagol was a Hobbit and his name largely defined his nature, as it means "burrowing, worming in". For even then, Sméagol was possessed by a restless and inquiring nature. He was always searching, and digging among the roots of things, burrowing, but also twisting and turning, this way and that. While fishing and exploring Stoorish Hobbit river lands east of the Misty Mountains, Sméagol's cousin Déagol (meaning "secret") discovered a gold ring lost on the river bottom.

Nonetheless, as the history of the One Ring is revealed, we eventually learn that Sméagol was immediately corrupted by its power. He murdered his cousin and took possession of the One Ring. Or, to be more accurate, the One Ring took possession of Sméagol and so began the transformation of Sméagol the Hobbit into Gollum the cannibalistic ogre. The evil power of the One Ring lengthened Sméagol's cursed life for centuries, yet it warped and corrupted him beyond recognition. Thereafter he was called Gollum because of the nasty guttural sounds he made when he spoke.

Gollum became a murderous ghoul and cannibal, shunning light and taking grim solace in dark caverns and dank pools.

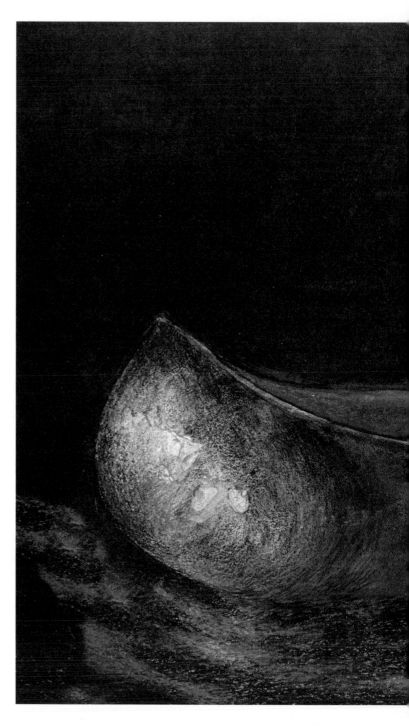

GOLLUM IN BOAT
LIDIA POSTMA

GOLLUM FALLS INTO THE CRACKS OF DOOM
MELVYN GRANT

GOLLUM
LIDIA POSTMA

The evolution of the character of Sméagol to that of Gollum draws on a considerable body of mythology related to Ring Legends. In the *Völsunga Saga*, the most famous ring legend in Norse mythology, we have Fáfnir the son of the Dwarf King Hreidmar who murders his own father in his desire to possess a cursed ring and its treasure. This is comparable to Sméagol's murder of his cousin Déagol in his own desire to possess the One Ring. Retreating like Sméagol to a mountain cave, Fáfnir broods over his ring and eventually transforms into a monstrous dragon. Similarly Sméagol, who through the power of the One Ring extends his life over the centuries, transforms into a ghoul twisted in mind and body into the cannibalistic Gollum brooding over his "precious" ring. The Icelandic narrative poem *Völundarkviða* reveals a similar ghoul in Sote the Outlaw. Sote steals a cursed ring but so fears it may be taken from him that he has himself buried alive with it, and sleeplessly guards it with his weapons drawn.

In Sméagol–Gollum we have a classic case of a split personality, as first portrayed in Robert Louis Stevenson's *Dr Jekyll and Mr Hyde* or in Charles Dickens' *The Mystery of Edwin Drood*. In Tolkien's case, it is not Jekyll and Hyde, but Sméagol and Gollum. When Sméagol is in control, he had pale eyes and referred to himself as "I". Gollum, however, was a green-eyed creature that called himself "we" because Gollum and the Ring spoke as collectively together. Just as in Stevenson's tale, it is this evil aspect of his being that was in perpetual conflict with that of the good. And just as in Stevenson's tale, the conflict leads to the destruction of both Sméagol and Gollum.

LÚTHIEN BEFORE MORGOTH
LIDIA POSTMA

THURINGWETHIL
MAURO MAZZARA

VAMPIRES

Blood-sucking creatures in folklore that feed on the blood of the living, usually taking the form of undead human beings and sometimes as "were-bats". Considering their powerful hold on the European imagination, they play surprisingly little part in Tolkien's legendarium, perhaps because he felt that they belonged so distinctly to a territory already amply occupied by Bram Stoker's *Dracula* (1897).

Batlike demons do, however, make a passing appearance in *The Silmarillion*, where they serve Morgoth. One especially powerful Vampire or bat-demon has a name, Thuringwethil, the "Woman of Secret Shadows", who inhabits the haunted tower of Tol-in-Gaurhoth. In *The Silmarillion*, Lúthien disguises herself as Thuringwethil in order to enter Angband.

In the First Age, too, Sauron also sometimes takes on a batlike form, dripping blood as he passes. Otherwise, these beings largely disappear from Tolkien's stories of later ages.

THE BEGUILING SURFACE LIDIA POSTMA

I first read Tolkien in the early seventies, when I studied graphic arts and painting at the Gerrit Rietveld Academie in Amsterdam. It was *The Hobbit* – still most dear to me and in which Tolkien develops his vast imagination – that opened up to me a panoramic view of what my illustrations might look like one day.

I decided to make it my final exam project, of which Bilbo's portrait was a vital part, as was Gandalf and Gollum in his boat.

A few years later, having completed my first own children's picture books, I was asked to participate in *A Tolkien Bestiary* by David Day. The subjects I was given made me dig in where I'd previously just touched on the beguiling surface.

EAGLE VS. DRAGON
KIP RASMUSSEN

EAGLE EMISSARIES

The Eagles, or Emissaries of Manwë, the king of the Valar, whose mansions are perched upon Taniquetil, the tallest mountain in the world. In the First Age, the Lord of Eagles is Thorondor whose wings measure 30 fathoms (54.8m [180ft]) and whose strength and power prove even greater than that of the mighty Dragons of Morgoth in that era-ending War of Wrath.

The Eagles of Manwë of Tolkienian mythology are consistent with the eagle emissaries of the Greek Zeus (and the Roman Jupiter) as the king of gods whose mansion stood on Mount Olympus, considered by the Greeks the tallest mountain in their world. Throughout Indo-European mythology, where the king of the gods is usually also a mountain and storm god, the eagle is typically found as one of his principal attributes or emblems. This also applied to the earthly rulers of most Eurasian empires. The aquila (eagle) was from early on associated with Roman imperial rule, carried as a standard by the Roman legions. And, subsequently, the Imperial Eagle was adopted by the Russian Czar, the German and Austro-Hungarian Kaisers, and the self-created emperor, Napoleon.

The Great Eagles of the Third Age are not a match in size to those of the First, but are nonetheless awesome birds capable of easily swooping down and carrying Men, Elves and Dwarves aloft in their grip. The intervention of the Giant Eagles in Tolkien's narratives is always crucial and climactic: they arrive at times of desperate need as, for example, in the Battle of the Five Armies in *The Hobbit*. They frequently appear when rescue can be achieved only by the power of flight, as in the rescue of Gandalf from Saruman's tower of Orthanc, and Frodo and Sam from Mount Doom.

In this way, the Eagles seem to serve as vehicles of destiny, as dei ex machina who, when all seems lost, appear almost out of nowhere to save the day. They are part of a long tradition of eagle-emissaries in myth and literature, leading from the birds of the Greek god Zeus to the vassals of Manwë, the Lord of the Winds of Arda.

ON MOOD KIP RASMUSSEN

There is indeed a dragon hoard of inspiring images and events hidden in Tolkien's work. But when it comes to the actual steps toward illustrating a scene, my question is always, what mood is set by the scene? Then, comes the decision as to which colours would best evoke this mood. Sometimes it's the blues of the starlit world, sometimes the greys of the northern mountains, sometimes the yellows after the advent of the sun, or maybe the orange of the blast of dragons. But it is always in the service of perhaps somehow enriching the stories for fellow fans of the world of Arda.

It is a joy and a privilege to illustrate the work of Tolkien. For me, the work of Tolkien is as serious, powerful and transformative as the work of Dostoyevsky, Hugo, Melville or any of the world's great authors. I hope it doesn't seem too extreme to call him the Vermeer, the Caravaggio, the Shakespeare, the Michelangelo of our age, an artist whose work will be examined and revered four hundred years from now, and beyond.

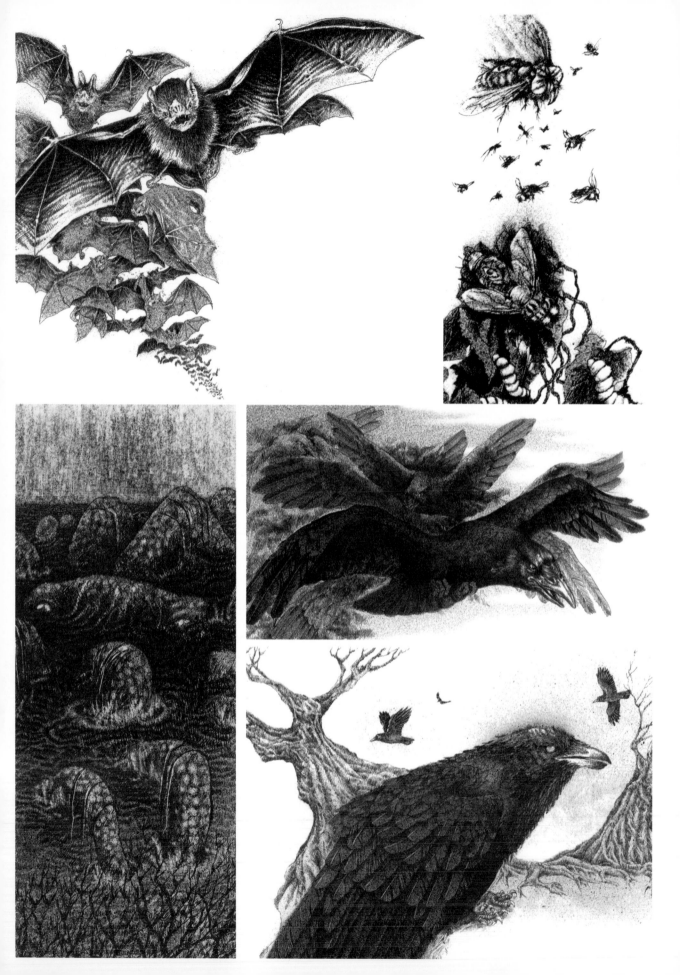

KELVAR
ALLAN CURLESS

TOLKIEN'S KELVAR
DAVID DAY

Tolkien's Middle-earth and the Undying Lands are the most elaborately conceived imaginary worlds in literature. And it appears extraordinarily complete in almost every aspect of its existence: from its geography and the history of its peoples, to the evolution of its many languages, and especially its ecology and natural history. Of course, *A Tolkien Bestiary* was a complete cataloguing of the enormous range of real or imagined or mythical fauna of Middle-earth. Large-scale creatures like Dragons, Balrogs, Trolls, Elves, Dwarves, Orcs, Men and Hobbits, for instance, were each assigned specific illustrators to have them appear unique and instantly visually recognizable as a species or race.

However, when it came to the task of illustrating many of the lesser fauna of Middle-earth, it was necessary to give some continuity to establish an assumed natural order of creatures within Tolkien's world. To this end, it was decided to consign these fauna to a single artist. Allan Curless proved to be the obvious choice when it was discovered that he already had considerable experience in illustrating wildlife. Ever adaptable, Allan took on the assignment with enthusiasm. He proved especially knowledgeable and inspired in his renderings of birds of all kinds. From the mighty Eagles of Manwë and gigantic Swans of Ulmo, to the Thrushes of Erebor and the tiny Tinuviel night singers. From the noble Ravens of Erebor to the evil Crebain and ignoble Gorcrows. There were also flights of bats and peculiar insects like the evil flies of Mordor marked with the Dark Lord's Eye and the strange noisy insects known to the Hobbits as Neekerbreekers. Allan Curless's imagination re-created them all.

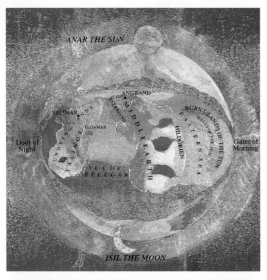

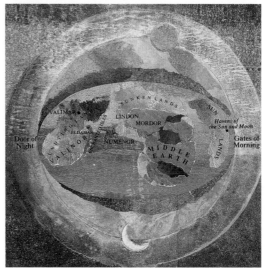

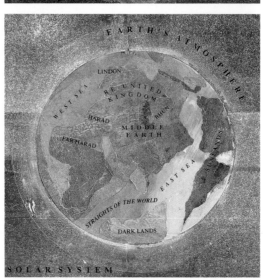

MAPPING ARDA   DAVID DAY

The mapping of Arda through time presented Sally Davies with a considerable challenge that is complicated by a number of quite unique problems. Although Arda is almost a biblical creationist world that does not entertain the idea of Darwinian evolution, it is definitely a world that embraces the ideas of Charles Lyle's geological evolution – and the later theory of continental drift – with a vengeance. The movement of continents in our primary (real) world took place over hundreds of millions of years; in Tolkien's world their movement takes place in the relatively rapid measure of tens of thousands of years.

MIDDLE-EARTH

The main continent in Tolkien's legendarium, in its northwestern regions, provides the primary setting for his epic tales. It is perhaps the most richly imagined land in fantasy fiction, meticulously detailed in terms of its geography, wildlife, peoples, cultures and, of course, histories.

That said, Tolkien always insisted that Middle-earth is our real world – the planet Earth in another incarnation. He acknowledges in several of his letters of the 1950s that the name often confused his readers: "Many reviewers seem to assume that Middle-earth is another planet!" He found this a perplexing conclusion because in his own mind he had not the least doubt about its locality: "Middle-earth is not an imaginary world. The name is the modern form of midden-erd > middel-erd, an ancient name for the oikoumene, the abiding place of Men, the objectively real world, in use specifically opposed to imaginary worlds (as Fairyland) or unseen worlds (as Heaven or Hell)." A decade later, Tolkien famously even gave a journalist an exact geographic location: "the action of the story takes place in North-west of Middle-earth, equivalent in latitude to the coastline of Europe and the north shore of the Mediterranean…"

The confusion that arises about Middle-earth can be attributed, however, not so much to a spatial issue, but a temporal one: a question not so much of where Middle-earth is, but when. "The theatre of my tale is this earth", Tolkien explained in one letter, "the one in which we now live, but the historical period is imaginary."

For an explanation, one must look to the chronicles of *The Silmarillion*. Tolkien's world begins with the command of Eru the One and a Great Music out of which comes forth a Vision like a globed light in the Void. This Vision becomes manifest in the creation of a flat Earth within spheres of air and light. It is a world inhabited by godlike spirits known as Valar and Maiar as well as newborn races including the Elves, Dwarves and Ents. We are 30,000 years into this history, however, before the human race actually appears in what Tolkien calls the First Age of Middle-earth. Another 3,900 years pass before the cataclysmic destruction of the Atlantis-like civilization of Númenor during Middle-earth's Second Age, which results in this mythical world's transformation into the globed world we know today.

THE MAPPING OF ARDA THROUGH TIME
SALLY DAVIES

THE UNDYING LANDS
JAMIE WHYTE

A ll in all, it takes some 37,000 years of chronicled history before the events described in *The Lord of the Rings* during the Third Age actually begin. And even after the War of the Ring in Middle-earth's Fourth Age, we are assured that many millennia will have to pass before Tolkien's archetypal world evolves into the real material world of recorded human history.

Tolkien himself estimated that his own time was some 6,000 years after Middle-earth's Third Age. Working backward from our own system of time, this would place the creation of Middle-earth and the Undying Lands at 41,000 BC while the War of the Ring appears to have taken place sometime between 4,000 and 5,000 BC in our historiographical system.

This is the real trick of Tolkien's Middle-earth: an imaginary time in the real world's age of myth that had a parallel existence and evolution just before the beginning of the human race's historic time. Tolkien's Middle-earth is meant to be something akin to what the ancient Greek philosopher Plato saw as the ideal world of archetypes: the world of ideas behind all civilizations and nations of the world.

VALINOR

I n Tolkien's legendarium the land of the immortal Valar and Maiar in the continent of Aman, surrounded, except to the west, by the mighty Pelóri Mountains, also known as the Undying Lands. Ruled by Manwë and Varda, the king and queen of the Valar, Valinor is comparable to Asgard, the home of the Norse gods ruled by Odin and Frigg, the king and queen of the gods, as well as to any number of mythological lands of the immortals.

Geographically, Valinor's/Aman's positioning to the far west of the continent of Middle-earth – at least in the First Age – recalls the continents of North and South America, which for Europeans during the early Age of Discovery (fifteenth to sixteenth century) was a New World full of wonders.

BELEGAER

T he "Great Sea" that separates the mortal lands of Middle-earth from the immortal lands of Aman. This Western Sea was essentially inspired by the Atlantic Ocean, though as it was known or imagined in the mythology and legends of the ancient Greeks and Celts. The drowned island of Atlantis, the paradisical Fortunate Isles, inhabited by the Greek heroes after their deaths, and the Irish phantom-island of Hy-Brasil were all considered to lie somewhere in the Atlantic. All were inspirations for the islands of Númenor and Tol Eressëa.

SUNRISE ON NÚMENOR
KIP RASMUSSEN

NÚMENOR

The large island in the Western Sea gifted to the Men of Beleriand by the Valar as reward for their part in the wars against Morgoth in the First Age. Ruled by a dynasty of kings descended from Elros, son of Eärendil, it flourishes for much of the Second Age but is ultimately destroyed, sinking back beneath the waves. In Númenor, we see a great civilization corrupted by power and pride slowly evolve into a tyranny that threatens the peace of the world and finally self-destruct.

Númenor is the most obvious example of the influence of the legends of the ancient Greeks on Tolkien's fiction. His tale *Akallabêth* ("The Downfall of Númenor") is Tolkien's reinvention of the ancient legend of Atlantis, related by the Greek philosopher Plato in his dialogues *Timaeus* and *Critias*. Atlantis, another island set in a western sea (in this instance the Atlantic), is portrayed as a lost utopian civilization that the gods eventually destroy because of the pride and folly of its people.

Like the myth of Atlantis, Númenor is a cautionary tale of the rise and fall of empires, a common trope since classical times. Not even the greatest civilizations last because pride and power ultimately corrupt. Every rise to power is inevitably followed by a fall and subsequent self-destruction. This is often due to the tragic flaw the Greeks called hubris, a combination of excessive pride, overconfidence and contempt for the gods. The fall of Tolkien's Númenor is exactly of this kind. The last king, Ar-Pharazôn, in his contempt for the Valar and desire for immortality, leads a fleet against Aman, prompting Eru, the One God, to cause the Change of the World: Arda is turned from being flat into a globe and Númenor sinks beneath the waves. The event is also somewhat akin to the biblical second Fall of Man in the Great Flood.

There may have been a more contemporary allusion to Tolkien's history of Númenor. Christopher Tolkien suggests that his father's portrait of the decline into a militaristic tyranny with imperial ambitions was an implicit comment on Nazism.

SUNRISE ON NÚMENOR   KIP RASMUSSEN

I am haunted by Númenor: a civilization powerful enough to defeat Sauron twice; a place which "astonished" the Dark Lord when he was brought there as a captive. Here was a being who had probably seen Valinor and Gondolin before its fall and was still shocked by the achievement of the Númenóreans.

Since the Númenóreans had been gifted both an undisturbed civilization for thousands of years and an extended life span, I thought that they would have had the time and vision necessary to create many colossi such as at the Argonath of Gondor. Although this scene is not described specifically in the work of Tolkien, I thought it was within the spirit of his magnificent creation of Númenor. I chose to depict this great civilization at its height since its destruction is one of the most wrenching moments in Tolkien's work. Here is Númenor at its "Sunrise".

LOTHLÓRIEN AND ENCHANTED FORESTS

Lothlórien is the fairest Elf-kingdom remaining on Middle-earth at the time of the War of the Ring, the domain of Galadriel and Celeborn. The name means "the land of blossoms dreaming". Lothlórien is also known as Lórien (perhaps meaning "dreamland") and Laurelindórenan ("the valley of the singing gold"). The domain echoes both Doriath, the domain of Thingol and Melian in Beleriand, and the Garden of Lórien in Valinor, whose trees Melian once tended.

Lothlórien is largely inspired by the ancient Celtic tradition of enchanted forests ruled by "white ladies". This enchanted forest of golden-leaved, silver-barked mallorn trees is protected by the power of the white-clad Galadriel, the possessor of Nenya, the White Ring of Adamant and Water. Using the power of the ring, Galadriel is able to keep her domain out of time, in a state of perpetual spring, immune to death and decay – a trope that allies it to many mythological paradises.

Such Celtic otherworlds were considered both potentially perilous and places of rest and healing. This ambiguity can be glimpsed in some views of Lothlórien in *The Lord of the Rings*, where the people of Gondor and Rohan are depicted as deeply suspicious of it and its ruler. Of the Golden Wood Boromir remarks, "few come out who once go in; and of that few none have escaped unscathed." Aragorn reproves this judgment, replacing "unscathed" with "unchanged". For the Fellowship of the Ring, it provides a place not only of rest and healing but also transformation, as we see in the Dwarf Gimli's change of heart in relation to the Elves.

GOLDEN WOOD OF LOTHLÓRIEN
DAVID KEARNEY

BIBLICAL EPICS DAVID KEARNEY

I worked as an illustrator in publishing for quite a number of years and painted images for a wide variety of books. Each commission was different and presented its own challenges and opportunities. I was pleased to be asked to produce a number of illustrations for the *World of Tolkien*.

Illustrating Tolkien's work is a great chance for an artist to use their imagination and paint visually dramatic paintings. The challenge for the illustrator is to come up with an image that is both original and appeals to the Tolkien readers who have their very own vision of Tolkien's world.

The illustrations for this book were painted at the time *The Lord of the Rings* films were hitting the big screen and were very much in the public eye. I tried very hard to distance myself from other popular Tolkien imagery and to keep the illustrations to my own view of Tolkien.

I considered each illustration as an individual piece, rather than a series of illustrations. My only overall aim was that I wanted to get the feel of a biblical epic. The starting point for each picture was a short piece of text describing the scene. I was then given a pretty free hand to create each illustration. I produced eight in total for the book, all painted in water-based gouache.

I had been illustrating a great number of children's adventure books at the time and the influence can be seen in the paintings. I also liked the drama in the paintings of John Martin and tried to introduce similar elements into the pictures. Looking back on the images now, I am still pleased with them and hope they are still enjoyed by readers of Tolkien.

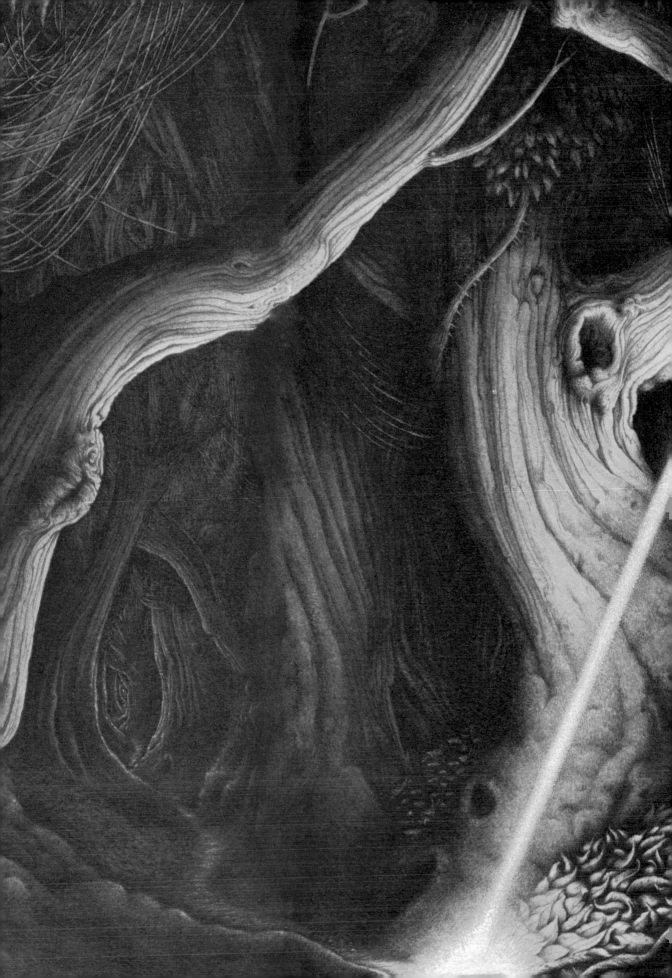

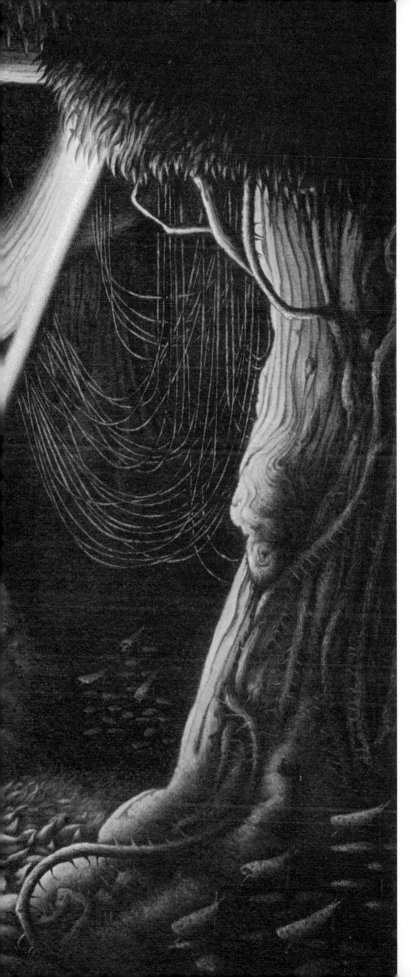

MIRKWOOD

A great forest in Rhovanion to the east of the Misty Mountains, home in the Third Age to Elves, Dwarves and Men, and, for a time, Sauron, the Necromancer of Dol Guldur.

This ancient Anglo-Saxon composite word conveys the lurking superstitious dread of primeval forests. In Germanic and Norse epic poetry, the dark forest is ever present and is even sometimes specifically given the name "Mirkwood". In the *Völsunga Saga*, Sigurd the Dragon-slayer enters Mirkwood and stops to mourn the loss of the "Glittering Heath", now ruined by the corruption of Fáfnir the dragon. The atavistic dread of the forest survives in many of the fairy tales of the Brothers Grimm, including "Little Red Riding Hood" and "Hansel and Gretel" and can be found too in Arthurian legend, where the forest represents a place of danger and dark magic but also transformation, the wild antithesis of the civilized court.

This theme of wilderness contaminated by evil is evident in Tolkien's own spider-infested Mirkwood. But it is also in Mirkwood that Bilbo Baggins twice saves the beleaguered Company of Dwarves and really proves his mettle, becoming the true hero of his own tale.

MIRKWOOD
PAULINE MARTIN

THE ENTS

Ents were treelike beings and "Shepherds of Trees" of Middle-earth, and among Tolkien's most original creations. Once asked about the origin of his Ents, Tolkien wrote: "I should say that Ents are composed of philology, literature and life. They owe their name to the eald enta geweorc of Anglo-Saxon." The Anglo-Saxon reference is to a fragment of the hauntingly beautiful Old English poem *The Wanderer*. The word *enta* there is usually translated "giant", so that the phrase means "old work of giants", and relates to the prehistoric stone ruins of Britain, then considered to be the work of an ancient race of giants. Out of such simple philological origins, Tolkien created beings of great and beguiling complexity – generally slow and gentle in their thoughts, words and deeds but capable of swift and elemental violence when roused, as in their overthrow of Isengard.

To find beings of myth and legend that correspond directly to the Ents, Tolkien had only to look back into English folklore, in which the Green Man plays such a key and distinctive part. Green Man stories and carvings are common in Tolkien's beloved West Midlands as well as in the Welsh Marches just beyond. The Green Man was in origin a Celtic nature spirit and tree god who represented the victory of the powers of growth over the powers of ice and frost. Essentially benevolent, he could also be powerful and destructive, just like the Ents and the even more belligerent Huorn tree spirits.

LIGHT   MAURO MAZZARA

Light is one of the things I most enjoy painting. Sunlight, and particularly daylight filtering through the trees in *Treebeard*. This total connection between Nature and the Ent. And then in *The March of the Ents*, the battle scene where the Ents are a ghostly presence looming up behind the battle smoke and haze of a foggy morning…I loved creating this piece.

HUORNS

The semi-sentient Huorns represent the wilder, more dangerous aspect of the Green Man: an inhuman power tapping the deepest sources of the natural world where fowls, animals and even children were sacrificed to placate the demonic spirit of certain trees.

The appearance of Huorns brought terror to their foes. They may have been Ents who in time had grown treeish, or perhaps trees that had grown Entish, but they were certainly wrathful, dangerous and merciless. In the Huorns, we have a dramatization of an avenging army of "Green Men" making an attack on all creatures who are hostile to the spirits of forests.

HUORNS
DAVID ROBERTS

TREEBEARD
DAVID ROBERTS

TREEBEARD

An Ent and, according to Gandalf, "the oldest living thing that still walks beneath the Sun upon this Middle-earth."

At 4.2m (14ft) tall, the "Shepherd of Trees" is among Tolkien's most original and eccentric heroes. Treebeard, or Fangorn (to use his Elvish name), resembles something between an evergreen tree and a man. The name Ent came from the Anglo-Saxon word *enta*, meaning "giant", while the portrayal of Ents (and of their wilder, more dangerous cousins, the Huorns) was inspired by Tolkien's extensive knowledge of the ancient lore and traditions of the Green Man.

Years after the publication of *The Lord of the Rings*, Tolkien in an interview acknowledged that the eccentric characterization of Treebeard was specifically meant as a good-humoured lampooning of his friend and colleague C. S. Lewis, the author of *The Chronicles of Narnia*, complete with his booming voice, his absurd "Hrum, hroom" interjections, and the authority of a complete know-it-all who, irritatingly, usually did know it all.

The Ents were also meant as a gentle satire of Oxford dons and particularly hidebound philologists more generally. Like those academics, Ents "were long on the discussion of problems, but slow to take action." Often, however, in both Oxford and in Entwood, action ultimately proved unnecessary as the debates often outlasted the problems. Ent gatherings, or "moots" with their qualifications, additions, exceptions and verbal footnotes on every point must have had a special savour for those who were familiar (as Tolkien was) with the editorial meetings of the compilers of the *Oxford English Dictionary*.

ENTS IAN MILLER

We had a lecturer at St Martin's in the 1960s who had an almost messianic obsession with teaching us colour theory. It got so intense I fled to the world of black and white and used nothing more, even in my degree show. About that time I'd also started using the Rotring technical pen which echoed the qualities I so loved in the etching process. The plus was I didn't need a print studio or printing press, just a table and chair and an idea. The Rotring technical pen became my tool of choice, and to a greater or lesser degree has remained so until today.

I left St Martin's with my head full of lines, an interest in all things architectural, and a love of story telling. Tolkien and Peake would not go away.

They offered a welcome point of reference and unassailable escape from the temporal grind; a visual kaleidoscope; history, myth and fantasy all rolled into one, with a myriad of creatures, people and places crying out to be drawn and painted. It was a wee bit like having a special toy box all over again. The 'F' expletive could join Fact and Fiction and run where they liked again.

First came an illustration of Gormenghast castle for a Ballantine fantasy calendar, then as a consequence, the animated feature *Wizards* and thereafter the opening sequence (short lived) for *The Lord of the Rings* in Los Angeles. *A Tolkien Bestiary* quickly followed. None of this was planned, it just happened that way. All I did was say "yes" to them all. It was all Tolkien then. Ralph Bakshi wanted me to go back to LA to work on his animated feature of *The Lord of the Rings* but I opted to go with the *Bestiary* and stay in the UK. Debra Zuckerman, the extremely clever art director, made it easy for me. She matched me up perfectly with the visual material and off I went, Rotring scratch pens in hand.

As I recall, the only thing I had to wait on, clearance-wise, was my first Ent illustration which had to be cleared by a diminutive expert on Ents living somewhere in New York. My imagination worked over time on that one. There was work pressure of course, given the number of images required, and I did on occasion starburst with the odd arboreal scream "F*** Hobbits" but I think it was more a raucous endearment than an indictment and nobody seemed much worried by it.

I never looked back after the diminutive expert gave me the thumbs up on my first Ent illustration, and I have never really stopped drawing them in one form or another ever since.

OLVAR
ALLAN CURLESS

←———→

TOLKIEN'S OLVAR　DAVID DAY

Few works of literature have landscapes as well-known and celebrated as Tolkien's Middle-earth. Many readers appear to know Tolkien's geography as well or better than many countries in the real world. In part this is because of the extraordinary care taken in his wonderful descriptions of the natural world. Just how remarkably detailed this world is evidenced by Tolkien's attention to its plants, flowers and trees.

When it came to the task of cataloguing the real or imagined flora of Middle-earth for *A Tolkien Bestiary*, we turned to the ever-adaptable Allan Curless who enthusiastically took on the job of illustrating what in Tolkien's world was known as the "Olvar" or "growing things rooted in the earth". Curiously enough, in recent years the botanist and Tolkien enthusiast Walter Judd in his "Flora of Middle-earth: Plants of Tolkien's Legendarium" has assiduously accounted for over one hundred and sixty plants that are to be found within the bounds of Arda.

Of these, many were unique inventions of Tolkien. And typically have multiple names in a variety of languages. Among Tolkien's flowers were the white star-flower Niphredil, the gold star flower Elanor and the sweet scented Lissuin that were often woven together as wedding garlands. Nothing is simple in the naming of things in Tolkien's world. Alfirin meaning "immortal" was the common name for the white or gold bell-shaped flowers that may – or may not – have been the same as the white bell-shape flower, known to the Rohirrim as Simbelmyne – an Old English construct meaning "Evermind" – that was known to the Sindar Elves as Uilos (meaning "everlasting snow").

As a lover of trees, Tolkien's original creations included the tallest trees upon Middle-earth in the silver-barked and golden-leafed Mallorn of Lorien and the mighty red-gold Culumalda of Cair Andros. But many real-world trees were given Elvish names: the birch was known as Brethil, beach was Neldoreth, holly was Region and willow as Tasarion.

There too Tolkien had his unique forms of herbs, such as Athelas or "Kingsfoil" a long-leafed plant that possessed remarkable healing powers, and was known to the Númenórean kings as Asea Aranion. And, of course, there was Tolkien's favourite, the Galenas plant, a leaf that was the beloved Pipeweed of the Hobbits that appears to be an obviously non-lethal form of what we now know as tobacco.

ATMOSPHERE   ANDREA PIPARO

I love nature and its life force. I firmly believe that there is a beauty as great as it is too little appreciated around us. I am fascinated by it – precisely because I feel it and recognize it – and I try to make detailed studies of it and observe its infinite variety in order to reproduce it in my works. I believe that a good representation of nature and setting is crucial in giving the right atmosphere to the illustration and always try to add a touch of magic and wonder that is typical of our world.

In *Haunted Barrow-downs* I wanted to create a dark and somewhat "silent" setting; as if time itself has stopped. Frodo realizes that he has entered the dismal valley in spite of himself, as he crosses the two huge vertical rocks at the entrance, and soon finds himself wrapped in a thick and cold fog. His comrades, Sam, Merry and Pippin, disappear into the thick grey blanket, and the poor Hobbit soon finds himself alone and frightened. The calls and cries to find his companions have no effect, and he is deceived by the echo of the voice that in turn seems to call it, and ends up being captured by a Barrow-wight. The setting described by Tolkien is gloomy and ghostly: the fog pervades and swallows everything, and we *know* that it is easy to get lost among those hills in which danger lurks and roams.

BARROW-DOWNS

Low hills in Eriador crowned with megaliths, tumuli and long barrows that are the ancient burial grounds of Men dating back to the First Age of Middle-earth. In the Third Age they become the Great Barrows of the kings of Arnor but in the wake of Arnor's destruction, they are invaded and haunted by evil spirits.

Tolkien took his inspiration for the Barrow-downs from Britain's monumental Neolithic earthworks and later Anglo-Saxon barrow graves, which in later times often became the focus of folktales and legends. The Neolithic long barrows and Bronze Age round barrows of Normanton Down, on a ridge just south of Stonehenge in Wiltshire, southwestern England, is one possible real-world source for Tolkien's Barrow-downs. Another candidate is an impressive Neolithic site just 32km (20 miles) from Oxford, locally known as Wayland's Smithy. Tolkien had visited the site in outings with his family and knew well the many myths relating to Wayland the Smith (the Old Norse Völundr), a Germanic figure who was inspirational in the creation of the Elven Telchar the Smith. Both were master sword smiths who forged weapons with charmed blades like those discovered by the Hobbits in the Barrow-downs.

In 1939, at about the time Tolkien was writing the opening chapters of *The Lord of the Rings*, archeologists made an extraordinary discovery in Suffolk of three Anglo-Saxon long barrow graves at a site called Sutton Hoo. Covering about 64,749.7m² (16 acres), the site had been occupied for more than three and a half millennia before becoming an Anglo-Saxon burial site. The excavation also revealed the richest treasure trove of Anglo-Saxon artifacts ever found. The discoveries at Sutton Hoo were as revelatory of the Anglo-Saxon world as the discovery of Tutankhamen's tomb was of the ancient Egyptian world.

BARROW-WIGHTS

Barrow-wights were the evil undead spirits that animate the bones of entombed Men in the Barrow-downs of Eriador. Early in *The Lord of the Rings*, one of the Barrow-wights briefly imprisons Frodo, Sam, Merry and Pippin in a barrow until Tom Bombadil frees them.

The Barrow-wights are not an original Tolkien creation since they already had a long history, especially in the sagas of the Norsemen. These Norse tales tell of encounters similar to those experienced by the Hobbits in which evil spirits with terrifying luminous eyes and hypnotic voices hold unwary travellers captive. Having paralyzed a victim with its skeletal grip, the wight performed rituals around the body before finally dispatching him using a sword, as a kind of bloody sacrifice.

A belief in haunted tombs and the cursed treasures of the dead is among the oldest of superstitions and also one of the most widespread. Truly bloodcurdling curses (meant as a deterrent to grave robbers) have been discovered written on the walls of Egyptian tombs. Other examples can be found in ancient cultures as different and mutually remote as China and Mexico. The Anglo-Saxons, too, had similar beliefs: after all, it is the disturbance of a barrow grave that leads directly to the death of Beowulf, the greatest hero in Anglo-Saxon literature.

BARROW-WIGHTS
IAN MILLER

MORDOR
GRAHAM BENCE

MORDOR AND THE BLACK COUNTRY

The terrible mountain kingdom of Sauron the Dark Lord throughout the Second and Third Ages. Within this realm Sauron forges the One Ring in the volcanic fires of Mount Doom and gathers vast armies of Orcs, Trolls, Uruks, Southrons and Easterlings, all in his mission to dominate and enslave the kingdoms of the Elves and Men of Middle-earth.

Tolkien likely derived the name for this evil kingdom from the Anglo-Saxon *morðor*, meaning "murder" or "mortal sin". This seems an appropriate name for an evil kingdom created as an engine for slaughter. However, in Tolkien's own invented languages Mordor means "Black Land" in the Sindarin Grey Elven tongue and "Land of Shadow" in the Quenya language of the Eldar.

Tolkien's Mordor may have been partly inspired by his experience of the heavily industrialized coal-mining and iron-smelting region of the West Midlands – just to the west of his childhood Birmingham home – known as the Black Country. This was the furnace room of the Industrial Revolution where days were made black with coal smoke and nights were made hellishly red with the flames of blast furnaces. In 2014 the Wolverhampton Art Gallery made a convincing bid for the Black Country being an inspiration for Sauron's kingdom through an exhibition entitled "The Making of Mordor".

Since Tolkien explained that his map of Middle-earth is essentially an overlay of the real-world map of Europe (though in an imaginary archetypal time), there have been many attempts at determining just where Mordor might be located in the real world. Among the suggestions are the mountainous regions of the Balkans or even Transylvania, famous as the home of Count Dracula. However, reading Tolkien's directions, a much more likely real-world location for Mordor might be the present-day emptied sea-bottom basin of the Black Sea.

THE WILDERNESS   KIP RASMUSSEN

Tolkien's environments overwhelm me, as do the characters in his stories. The lands in his stories are often adversaries in the journeys of his heroes, and the great, desolate places often defeat the magnificent characters. Witness Caradhras, the Dead Marshes, the Old Forest, Mirkwood and Mordor. This idea of a heroic figure in a hostile wilderness is stirring, whether it's the Echoriath of Gondolin, or the forested highlands of Dorthonion. In fact, the descriptions of the trees and rivers are often more complete than that of the characters. We know, I think, more about the traits of a Mallorn than the specific appearance of Turin or Fingon.

THE SHIRE
JAMIE WHYTE

SHIRES

First created by the Anglo-Saxons in reference to counties in central and southern England under the authority of the "shire reeve" or sheriff. In modern times, the shires are rural or outlying counties not under the authority of a metropolitan council. Commonly, even today, the shires of the rural Midlands are considered strongholds of traditional rural culture. Tolkien's idealized childhood memories of the shires of the rural West Midlands inspired his fictional Hobbit homeland of "the Shire" in *The Hobbit* and *The Lord of the Rings.*

The Shire was Tolkien's romanticized analogy for the rural and pre-industrial English shires of his late Victorian childhood. His Hobbits were styled on the yeomen of England's "green and pleasant land." His Hobbits were to the tilled fields and rolling farmlands what Dwarves were to the mountains or the Elves to the forests: the genies, or guardian spirits, of the place. "The Shire is based on rural England and not any other country in the world", Tolkien once wrote. It was also, he added, "a parody of rural England, in much the same sense as are its inhabitants: they go together and are meant to. After all, the book is English, and by an Englishman." At the same time, there is a serious intent on Tolkien's part to create in his Hobbit homeland a place that embodies the enduring spirit of that ideal "little England" characterized by the lands and villages of the English shires.

The Shire is shaped like a child's wobbly drawing of the large front wheel of an old-fashioned penny-farthing bicycle and has a diameter measurement roughly equal to 40 or 50 leagues (193km to 241km [120 to 150 miles]). The four great spokes of the wheel radiate out from the hob and divide the Shire into four regions known as the Four Farthings. This is logical enough as a farthing comes from the Old English *feorthing*, meaning fourth or a fourth part. This is because the silver penny was marked with a cross on the reverse and each of these quarters was a farthing. The central hob of the Shire is marked geographically with a large standing stone, known as the Farthingstone.

HOBBITON

Hobbit village and ancestral home of the Baggins family of Bag End, located almost at the centre (or midland) of the Shire, not too far away from the Three-Farthing Stone.

The fictional Hobbiton was inspired by Tolkien's childhood memories of the then-rural Worcestershire village of Sarehole, six-and-a-half kilometres (four miles) from industrial Birmingham in the West Midlands. With his mother and his brother, from the age of four to eight (between 1896 and 1900) he lived at 5 Gracewell Road in the village. The green, pleasant farmland, fields and the woods of Sarehole with its nearby water-driven mill, were deeply imprinted on Tolkien's imagination and resurfaced in his creation of Hobbiton, which likewise has a water-driven mill, as we can see in the foreground of the lovely painting he made of *The Hill: Hobbiton-across-the-Water* (1937) as an illustration for *The Hobbit.*

In 1968 Tolkien made a contribution toward the restoration of Sarehole's eighteenth-century mill, and in 2002 a blue commemorative plaque was placed on it, funded by the Tolkien Society and the Birmingham Civic Society.

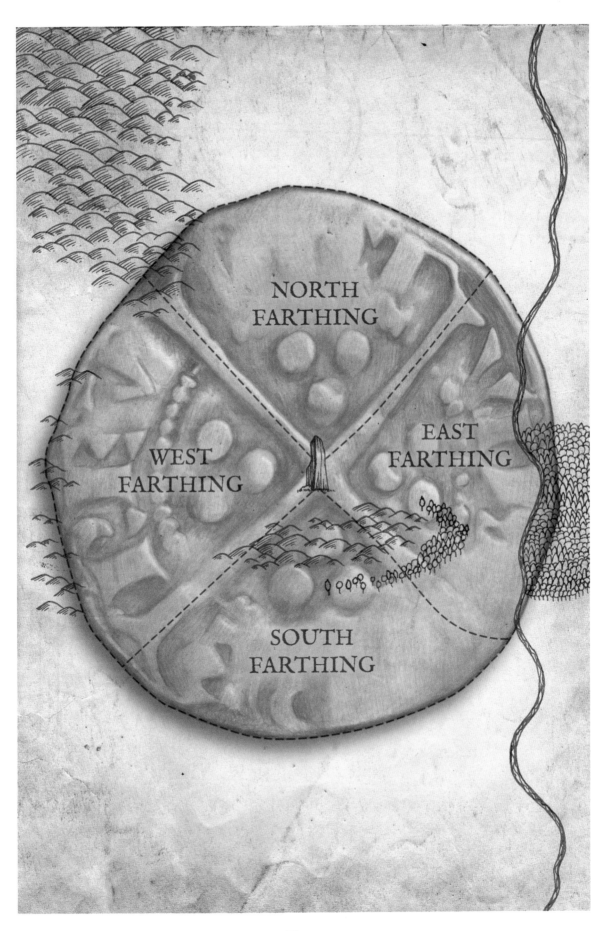

NORTH
FARTHING

WEST
FARTHING

EAST
FARTHING

SOUTH
FARTHING

NOT OVERDOING IT LIDIA POSTMA

Coming from children's books, and fairy tales in particular, I felt *A Tolkien Bestiary* was my opportunity to test and expose my skills and develop my artistry. Because it is all a big test for us illustrators, isn't it? Which is nauseating. The big challenge in "doing" Tolkien is not "overdoing" Tolkien.

It only gradually becomes clear where the boundaries are (your own limits, I mean) after much trying and failing…you go where you are most at ease.

In my case, I was most at ease with Hobbits and in and amongst the Hobbit landscape. And, if I'm honest, for me it is all about that fair island opposite Europe: the splendid isolation of the British kingdom, the particular Englishness exposed in Hobbit daily life. I find it so charming and endearing – enough to model my Hobbit illustrations in its image.

My first Hobbit landscape was inspired by a watercolour presented on the cover of a Penguin pocket edition of *Scenes of Clerical* life by George Eliot. Then later, I was inspired by good old Pieter Bruegel the Elder – his gregarious subjects, and those landscapes you can get lost in, because you always feel they are accessible to wander around in – as amazed as he must have been about them before he could draw and paint them. So, this was the thing I had to create – an accessible Hobbit landscape!

When gathering attributes for the scenes you want to depict, you become a sort of puppeteer of your favourite doll. The one you know inside out and endlessly turn the head and move the limbs of. It is all about the stage at which a child *knows* he is a part of the universe – without a syllable of a word in his head – and this magical state envelops and swallows up everything and everyone. It does not last, but Tolkien has struck the chord of a vivid memory of it. A childlike existence; almost innocent in its self-containing prosperity but yet there appears to be a whole world outside its borders, that one is only (and disturbingly) made aware of by *intruders*.

HOBBITON ON THE HILL
LIDIA POSTMA

←———→

UNCHARTED TERRITORY

LIDIA POSTMA

All of my artwork on Tolkien's world was conceived well before the age of the (personal) computer and before the exhausting possibilities of the medium as shown in movies of his books. In this I consider myself lucky. It is a privilege to work in uncharted territory as opposed to plod along a well trodden (and downtrodden) path…I am grateful for that!

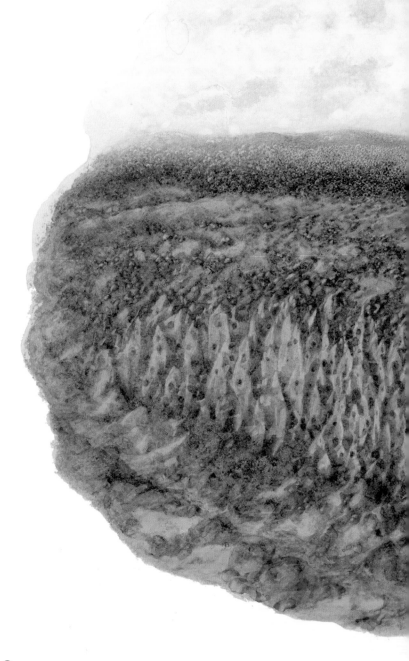

THE GREAT SMIALS
LIDIA POSTMA

LONELY MOUNTAIN

ANDREA PIPARO

In *Lonely Mountain* we see Thorin Oakenshield (the expedition's leader), the Dwarves, Bilbo and the sorcerer Gandalf proceeding on horseback towards Erebor, the kingdom inside the Lonely Mountain.

When creating this image I sought inspiration in the beauty of nature and tried to evoke, as effectively as possible, the magical spectacle that is created when the sun dyes the snow-capped peaks with orange at sunset.

I wanted to emphasize the majesty of the mountain and the fact that reaching it was the goal of the whole adventure: highlighting it with bright and clear colours, ensuring it was the most visible and important element of the whole composition.

As a fan of Tolkien's writings, I always try to be as faithful as possible to his descriptions. It is my opinion that an illustrator should be committed to the work of an author and try to remain as close as possible to the idea of a character or scene that the creator has provided.

As for my Tolkien illustrations, after first imagining the situation I intend to depict, I take care to refer back to the text to get as close as I can to his descriptions. I want to leave very little to my imagination for the final rendering, as personal style makes the interpretation unique in itself.

LONELY MOUNTAIN

ANDREA PIPARO

ANDUIN
LINDA GARLAND

←———≺

BEFORE AND AFTER THE FALL   DAVID DAY

As Tolkien has observed in literature and in life, there is no story without a fall. In the Quest of the Ring, the mighty Raurus Falls is the geographic setting for the fall – both physical and moral – of the noble but flawed hero Boromir, but also it is the setting for the breaking of the bond of trust and brotherhood for all of the members of the Fellowship of the Ring. In these two visions of Boromir's funeral boat being sent over the falls, the artists Linda Garland and Andrea Piparo have chosen quite different perspectives separated by just a few seconds in time. And the resulting illustrations result in quite different emotional responses. Linda Garland's vision-like landscape and the still water above the falls is a kind of beautiful requiem to Boromir that holds him back from the edge of oblivion. Andrea Piparo's conveys something of the great adventure of the Ring Quest as the funeral boat tips over the edge. It is a literal cliff-hanger moment that conveys the importance of the event and the spectacle and natural wonder of this setting on the edge of the mighty Rauros Falls.

RAUROS
ANDREA PIPARO

Rauros Falls depicts the great river Anduin where it is divided by the large rocky island of Tol Brandir and then continues over the Rauros waterfalls.

The shores that line the great river were the scene of the last goodbye that the Company gives Boromir, son of Denethor, following his death in the terrible battle with the Orcs. Legolas, Gimli and Aragorn laid their companion's body on the elven boat and honoured their friend by surrounding him with the trophies of his defeated enemies, before releasing the boat to the current.

I wanted to show the waterfalls in all their massive and natural power, at the precise moment when the boat bearing Boromir's body – tiny against the swell of the river – tilts to descend and disappear forever in the roar of the waters.

RAUROS FALLS
ANDREA PIPARO

UMBAR AND CARTHAGE

Port city to the south of Gondor and of the mouth of the Anduin River. For a thousand years a colony of Númenor, then a base for the Black Númenóreans, and later part of the Gondorian empire. By the time of the War of the Ring, Umbar had long been in the hands of the marauding Corsairs.

Umbar plays a similar role in the history of Gondor to the port-city of Carthage in the history of Rome. A colony of the mighty sea power of Phoenicia for a thousand years, Carthage rose to be an independent and significant power in the wake of the destruction of the Phoenician island city-state of Tyre in 332 BC (here a counterpart for Númenor). Just as Carthage and Rome vied for control of the Mediterranean, Gondor vied with Carthage for control over the vast Bay of Belfalas. The Black Númenórean Lords of Umbar (whose war fleets were the terror of the seas and whose powerful mercenary armies were buttressed by divisions of war elephants) were a torment over many lands. The lords of Carthage (whose mighty war fleets were the terror of the seas and whose powerful mercenary armies were buttressed by war-elephants) were a torment over many lands.

In the Third Age, after centuries of rivalry, the Ship Kings of Gondor engaged in century-long wars (933–1050 TA) on sea and land, which resulted in the eventual conquest and subjugation of Umbar and its Southron Empire of Harad. This is similar to Rome's century-long Punic Wars (256–146 BC) on sea and land, which resulted in the eventual conquest and subjugation of Carthage and its North African empire. The Black Númenórean rulers of Umbar were slain or scattered, and the city and port served as Gondor's southern fortress controlling its vast Haradrim territories. The Carthaginians, too, were slain or sold into slavery, and its city and port served as Rome's southern fortress controlling its vast North African territories.

Subsequently, Tolkien's chronologies inform us that Umbar slipped from Gondor's grasp after five centuries. In the year 1448 TA Gondorian rebels and lords among the Haradrim captured Umbar. These new lords became known as the Corsairs of Umbar, and their mighty pirate fleets once again terrorized the seas, harassing and attacking Gondor and its allies.

THE CORSAIRS OF UMBAR
ALLAN CURLESS

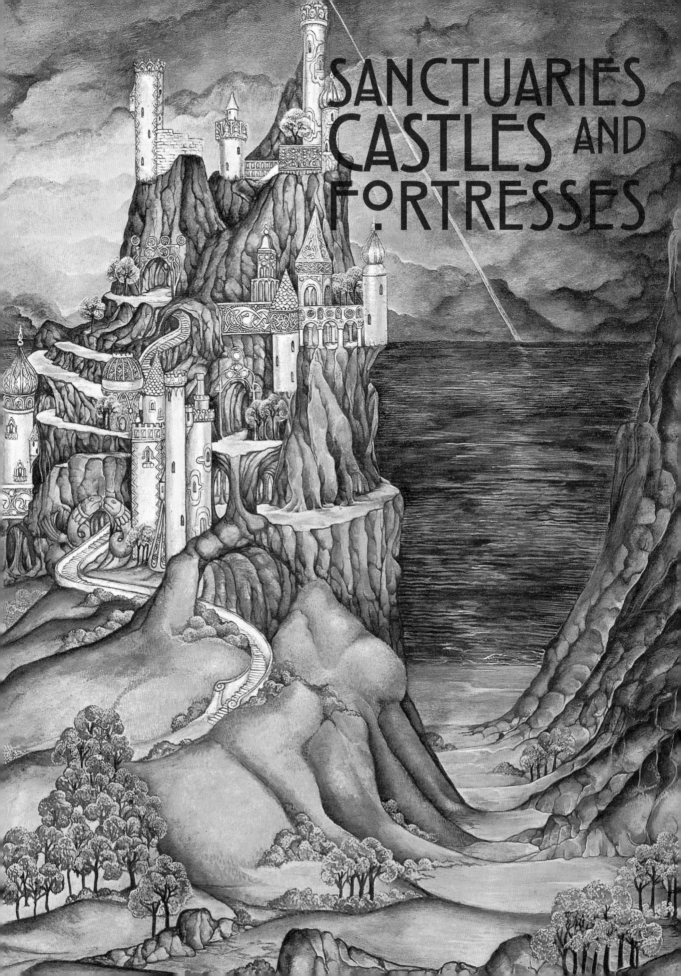

SANCTUARIES
CASTLES AND
FORTRESSES

↑ THE FALL OF BARAD-DÛR
DAVID KEARNEY

TIRION
LINDA GARLAND

CASTLES

To the Romans the stronghold or fortification was called a castrum. To the Anglo-Saxons it was a castel; while to the medieval English it was a castle. In history, myth and fiction, the castle, hill fort, citadel or walled town is a dramatic manifestation of a nation's stern power and high romance. It is the centre of life and is the idealized world in a microcosm. It protects the seat of earthly power, the throne, it contains the symbol of heaven, the chapel, and it threatens with the symbol of hell, the dungeon.

The character of that enclosed world is determined by the master who builds and commands it. Outwardly it might be seen as a mandala or a maze: a saint's paradise or a demon's labyrinth. A place of peace and safety, or a hell on earth. Whether as a place to storm or a place to defend, the castle is the symbol of spiritual strength. The forces of light or darkness, good or evil, life and death are implicit in that struggle.

That the castle in all its metaphoric implications was understood by all who lived in the great ages of castles cannot be doubted. As Tolkien knew well enough, the oldest surviving morality play (pre-dating *Everyman*) is *The Castle of Perseverance*. Here, despite a siege army of the Deadly Sins and the Forces of Hell, Man was secure. The evil enemy for all its might cannot overwhelm the Castle. So long as he stays in it, he is safe, but if he is tempted to go outside, he may face eternal damnation. The meaning of the castle is direct and unmistakable, and it is an allegory as much psychological as moral.

In the writing of J R R Tolkien we have the most fully realized and extensive invented world of castle-kingdoms and fortified strongholds in modern fantasy fiction. Tolkien's world of Middle-earth was created by an imagination fuelled by a massive knowledge of mythologies and histories of the castle-kingdoms of Europe. Although Tolkien himself denied any allegorical intention in his work, his theme is that most ancient struggle, never to be resolved, between the powers of good and evil.

In the wide lands of Middle-earth, the kingdoms of Elves, Dwarves and Men are at war with the dreadful forces of Sauron, the Dark Lord of Mordor. The centre and source of power in the mountain-ringed land of Mordor is the massive Barad-dûr, the Dark Tower of Sauron. From this tower Sauron commands his legions of Orcs, Uruks, Trolls and the damned spirits of barbarian men.

TOLKIEN THE ARCHITECT KIP RASMUSSEN

Tolkien was a master of visual design and even architecture. How did he contrive a city of seven levels, such as Minas Tirith? Or design a setting such as the caldera of an extinct volcano as was the Vale of Tumladen in which the city of Gondolin was built? How did he invent cities underground such as Menegroth, Nargothrond, Moria and Erebor? How did he conceive of the mighty Pillars of Argonath? This was a creator who was not just a master of literature, but of visual conception as well.

ON CASTLES AND HIGH WALLS
IAN MILLER

Castles and high walls, places of refuge, never cease to intrigue me. Whether they be of stone, baked mud, palisades of timber, water-packed sand or mere metaphors and transports of the mind. Build them up, knock them down; the interest and fascination never goes away.

Castles, like Ents, are something I seem to draw a lot of. I often wonder if it's the mere architecture and structural constraints of such places that interests me, or the stories that shape and define them. Given the often impossible perspective I use and the obtuse angles that defy the working constraints of even the most outrageous flying buttresses, I suspect it is the latter.

THE DESTRUCTION OF MORDOR
ALLAN CURLESS

MINAS TIRITH
GRAHAM BENCE

MINAS TIRITH

The "Tower of the Guard" is the greatest surviving city and fortress of Gondor at the time of the War of the Ring. Originally known as Minas Anor, the "Tower of the Setting Sun", it is a citadel built on a hill with seven levels, seven concentric walls and seven gates, each facing a different direction. It is mostly made out of white stone, except for the lowest wall, which is made of the same impervious black stone as Orthanc.

The Gondorian capital is comparable to the imaginary City of the Sun, a utopia devised in 1602 by the Renaissance friar and philosopher Tommaso Campanella (1568–1639): "The greater part of the city is built upon a high hill, which rises from an extensive plain, but several of its circles extend for some distance beyond the base of the hill, which is of such a size that the diameter of the city is upward of two miles, so that its circumference becomes about seven. [...] It is divided into seven rings or huge circles named from the seven planets..." The City of the Sun, however, has only four principal gates, positioned at the compass points in the lowest wall – an arrangement that Tolkien considerably refined upon at Minas Tirith.

Both Minas Tirith and the City of the Sun look back to ancient mythological traditions: the ancient Sumerians believed that there were seven walls and seven gates to both heaven and hell, and the biblical paradise of Eden was surrounded by seven walls entered through seven gates. There are connections, too, with the ancient tradition of the Music of the Spheres and the divine order of the universe – a tradition that fascinated Tolkien deeply.

Ultimately in the War of the Ring, against this sea of darkness, one realm stands fast, the citadel and walled city of Minas Tirith, the White Tower of Gondor. It is here, before the seven ring walls of the White Tower, that the greatest battle would rage, and the tide of war would be turned against the Dark Lord.

However, it is only when the Dark Tower itself is toppled and entirely obliterated that the War of the Ring would be ended. Only then would the White Tower become the centre of a new world of peace and prosperity, a monument to all that is good and great in the world.

UTUMNO
IAN MILLER

UTUMNO

The mighty subterranean fortress of Melkor, the Black Enemy, beneath the Iron Mountains in the northern wastes of Middle-earth. Utumno means "hidden depths" in Quenya, while its Sindarin name is Udûn, meaning "dark pit". It is in Utumno that Melkor gathers rebel Maiar, monstrous demons and other evil spirits about him and breeds the first Orcs in mockery of the Elves, and from which he wages war against the Valarian Powers of Arda before the first rising of the moon and the sun.

Utumno's various names connect it to Tartarus in Greek mythology. In the *Iliad* Homer situates Tartarus below Hades (the Underworld) so deep and dark that one would not reach its bottom for a year. Rather than being a fortress for evil and chaos, however, it is conceived of their prison, into which Zeus, king of the gods, has thrown the Titans after he has defeated them in the Titanomachy, the primordial war between the Olympian gods and the rebel Titans.

In John Milton's *Paradise Lost* Tartarus is the name given to the subterranean fortress of Satan and the fallen angels and is thus a direct counterpart to Utumno.

TULKAS IN UTUMNO
MAURO MAZZARA

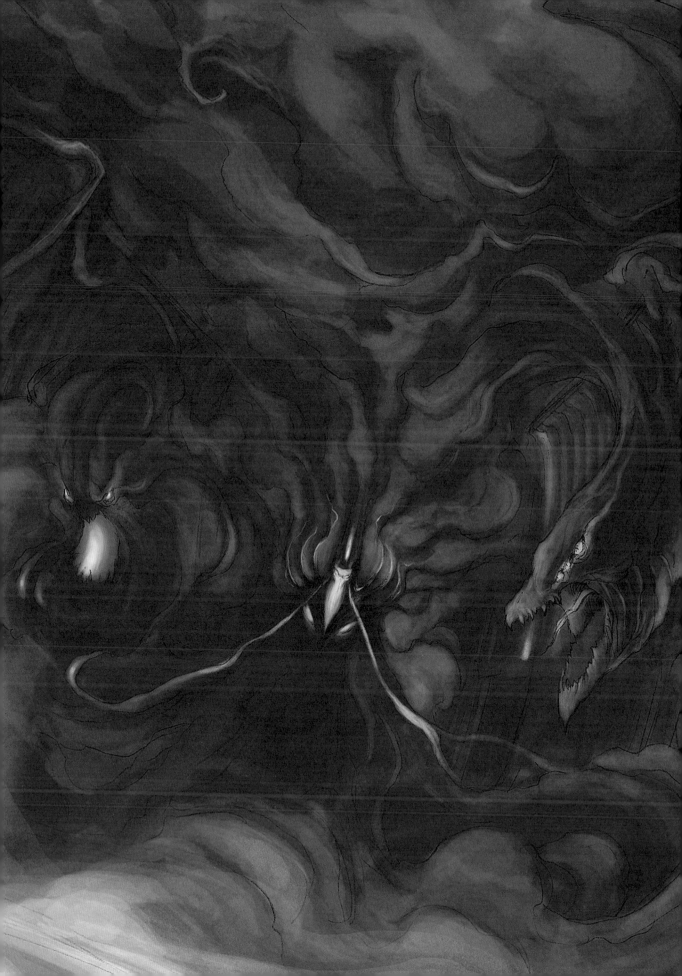

MORIA
IAN MILLER

←——————→

KHAZAD-DÛM

Khazad-dûm, or Dwarrowdelf, is the greatest and grandest of all the mansions and mines of the Dwarves in Middle-earth. Founded by Durin the Deathless, the first of the Seven Fathers of the Dwarves in the Ages of Stars, Khazad-dûm in the Misty Mountains encompasses the greatest mines in Middle-earth, famous for their rich seams of mithril, the "silver steel" that is worth ten times its weight in gold.

We can only speculate about the inspirations for this magnificent Dwarvish kingdom. We know for sure that the great three peaks above Khazad-dûm were inspired by a walking vacation in the Alps as a young man. The origins of the mines beneath are more doubtful. There are many legends of lost mines around the world, most notably King Solomon's Mines, which supplied the biblical king with his fabulous wealth. On the more realistic side of things, Tolkien grew up not far from the Black Country in the Midlands, home to hundreds of coal pits (though coal is hardly comparable to the precious and beautiful mithril).

Whatever its origins, Khazad-dûm thrives until the year 1980 of the Third Age when the Dwarves delve too deep in search of mithril and an entombed Balrog is released within the halls of the Dwarves. So terrible was the Balrog's strength and wrath that the Dwarves were driven from their kingdom. Thereafter, the abandoned realm is known by its Elvish name of Moria, the "Black Pit".

THE WALLS OF KHAZAD-DÛM ↑
SUE PORTER

DWARVES OF BELEGOST AND ELVES OF MENEGROTH
DAVID DAY

In the contrasting illustrations of Ian Miller's *Belegost* and Linda Garland's *Thousand Caves of Menegroth*, we see the essential difference between the fortress-building Dwarves and the sanctuary-seeking Elves.

Both races have wealthy and thriving subterranean kingdoms and both live under the existential threat from their fellow cave dwellers such as Dragons, Trolls and Orcs. However, their focus on life and their choice of defences are quite different.

Dwarves are hoarders, master forgers of weapons and stonemasons who believe their fortifications are essential to their survival and wealth. Elves are capable of similar feats with metal and stone, but depend primarily upon powerful spells of enchantment to guard their kingdom. Unlike the Dwarves, they make no displays of power or weapons of war, but spend their creative powers and arts on the imitation of nature, filling their realm with trees, birds and animals carved from stone, with their halls and chambers filled with fountains and lamps of crystal.

BELEGOST
IAN MILLER

TOLKIEN AND US
LINDA GARLAND

To be commissioned for *A Tolkien Bestiary* so early on in my career was very exciting, and to be in the company of fine, contemporary illustrators was an honour, if a little daunting. My problem was that as a "rookie" illustrator (I had only been with the agency for a few months) I was literally not up to speed and the schedule demanded my artworks be oil sketches rather than my favoured oil paintings.

I have always been an avid reader – rather eclectic in taste – but there are two books that have changed my life and inspired my work. The first being *The White Goddess* by Robert Graves – it's what he leaves out and not what he puts in that is able to fire my imagination. The second is of course *The Lord of the Rings* by J R R Tolkien. This classic book of epic proportions has run through my life, and especially the life of my late husband Roger Garland, who produced over forty illustrations for the publishers of J R R Tolkien. Together, we opened our gallery in 1987 showing the permanent exhibition of Roger's Tolkien illustrations alongside our other work and have met some lovely people along the way.

Looking back, Menegroth is my favourite of the artworks I produced for *A Tolkien Bestiary*. Back then, I enjoyed the challenge of conjuring up the strange and fantastical landscapes that set the scenes for Tolkien's imaginary world, and *Menegroth* captures that interest.

I have always painted in oils and still work every day, although I have gone back to my old ways and take months and not days to produce a painting.

MENEGROTH

LINDA GARLAND

AGLAROND AND CHEDDAR GORGE

Meaning "Caves of Glory" in Sindarin (Grey Elvish), Aglarond is the name given to the spectacular caverns in the White Mountains, close to Helm's Deep. Aglarond, as translated from the common tongue of Westron, is known as the "Glittering Caves".

Initially a fortress built by the Númenóreans, the Glittering Caves became a refuge for the Rohirrim, and later, in the wake of the War of the Ring, a new colony of Durin's Folk.

Tolkien acknowledged that the caves were inspired by the vast real-world caves of Cheddar Gorge in the Mendip Hills of Somerset, in southwestern England. One of the greatest "natural wonders" of Britain, this vast limestone gorge and cave complex is the site of some of the island's earliest Paleolithic human remains. Aglarond and the Cheddar Gorge and Caves both appear to have been formed by underground rivers, and their vast galleries contain deep reflecting pools with remarkable stalactite and stalagmite formations. Tolkien was known to have visited Cheddar Gorge and its caves on at least two occasions: in 1916, while on his honeymoon, and again in 1940.

DWINDLING POWER

The Sidhe were the remnant of the once mighty prehuman race of Irish immortals known as the Tuatha Dé Danann or the "People of the Goddess Danu". The Sidhe (pronounced "Shee") or the Aes Sidhe, meaning "People of the Hills", were believed to be those immortals who withdrew from the mortal realm and most often hid themselves away inside "hollow hills" and ancient burial mounds. However, other Sidhe lived hidden away and trapped in time in enchanted woodlands and kingdoms beneath lakes and in river grottos.

Tolkien's theme of the dwindling power of the immortal Elves upon the mortal lands of Middle-earth has much in common with the Aes Sidhe "People of the Hills". With Tolkien's Elves, we have kingdoms and cities that are comparable to many of those in the legends of the Sidhe hidden away in all manner of places. In the First Age the Sindar, Elves were found in the enchanted forest of Doriath and the glittering caverns of Menegroth. Noldor refuges were also hidden in the secret mountain passes of Gondolin, in precarious river gorges of Nargothrond, in the havens of Brithombar and Eglarest, and in the distant island refuge of Balar. The Second and Third Ages saw the establishment of the hidden realms of Lindon and the Grey Havens, the deep valley refuge of Imladris and the enchanted golden forest of Lothlórien.

Ultimately, Doriath does not survive into the Second Age. Menegroth is sacked and King Thingol is treacherously murdered by the Dwarves of Belegost over a dispute about the possession of a Silmaril. Melian abandons the kingdom, and, without the protection of her enchantment, Doriath is no longer protected against invasion by Orcs, Balrogs and Dragons. Total ruin ultimately comes in the wake of the War of Wrath when almost all of Beleriand is broken apart and swallowed up by the Western Sea. Like the Welsh Cantref y Gwaelod in Cardigan Bay or the Cornish Lyonesse near the Isles of Scilly, Doriath and Beleriand may be numbered among those "lost and drowned kingdoms" that abound in the legends of the Celtic fringes of the British Isles.

ATTACK AT THE FORD AT RIVENDELL
ALLAN CURLESS

RIVENDELL
MELVYN GRANT

HIDDEN VALLEYS

The steep hidden valley and Elven refuge of Master Elrond Half-Elven and his people. Considered the "Last Homely House East of the Sea", for four thousand years Rivendell (known as Imladris in Sindarin) is a refuge of wisdom and great learning for all Elves and Men of goodwill.

Rivendell, as a place of learning, takes some of its inspiration from Tolkien's own university city of Oxford, and, as a place of almost oracular wisdom and counsel, from ancient Delphi in Greece. Topographically, however, it seems to have been inspired – as shown in Tolkien's sketches and watercolours of Rivendell – by the spectacular deep-cloven Lauterbrunnen Valley, which the 19-year-old author-to-be encountered while on a walking tour in the Swiss Alps.

Perhaps the most convincing circumstantial evidence for this association might be a linguistic one. The river that cuts through Rivendell's steep valley is the Bruinen, a Westron name that Tolkien more often translates and refers to as the Loudwater River. Consequently, Middle-earth's Bruinen matches up rather well with the Swiss Lauterbrunnen: *lauter*, meaning "louder", and Brunnen, meaning "fountain, spring". Thus Lauterbrunnen, in one theory, simply translates as "louder water".

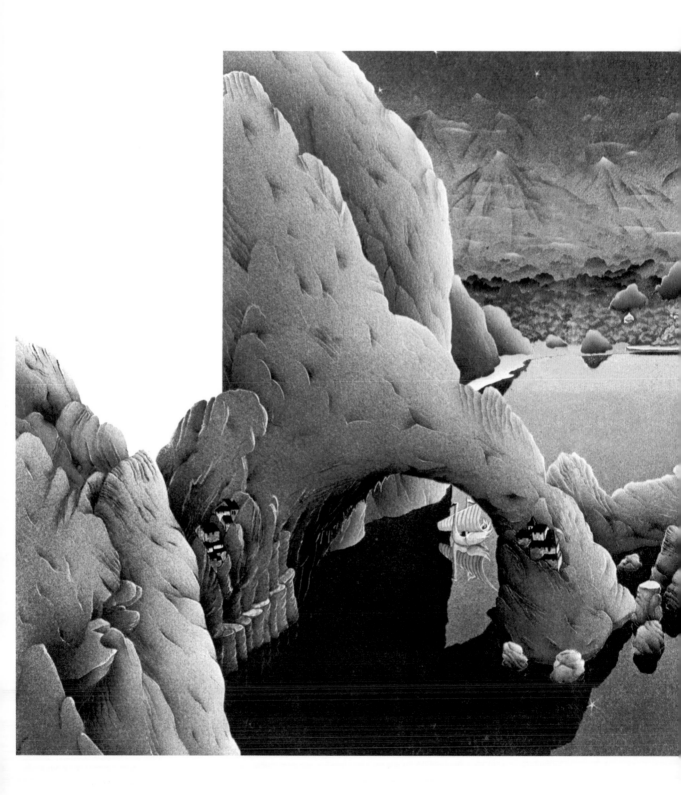

ALQUALONDË

The Third Kindred of the Eldar was led into the Undying Lands by King Olwë. These were the Teleri, or "those who come last". Tolkien's classification of the Elves in terms of "kindreds" appears to come from the Welsh faerie spirits known as the Tylwyth Teg, or "beautiful kindred". The Teleri were the most numerous of the three kindreds and so loved the sea and the stars that they wished to settle on the starlit shores of Eldamar. On Tol Eressëa, the "Lonely Isle", in the Bay of Eldamar, Olwë founded Avallónë as the island's principal port and city. Soon other cities prospered on the island, and Olwë eventually explored the north coast where he founded the greatest city of the Teleri – Alqualondë, the Haven of Swans.

SEA HAVENS
DAVID DAY

Sue Porter's soothing, dream-like water-colour washes evoke a serene sense of calm and reflective beauty in her starlit vision of this haven of the Sea-Elves of Eldamar. These were the first people to build ships and sail the seas. The "Haven of Swans" was so called because their ships were crafted in the elegant form of great white swans with wing-like sails. Beneath the arch of sea-carved stone, at the entrance to the natural harbour that is the gateway to this paradise, these immortals set out in starlight in their swan ships through enchanted isles and across the shadowy seas.

ALQUALONDË
SUE PORTER

BAG END

The Hobbit hole (smial) and ancestral home of the Baggins family of Hobbiton in the Shire. Bag End was the original name for Tolkien's aunt Jane Neave's Dormston Manor Farm, just a few miles from the author's childhood home in the hamlet of Sarehole in what was then rural Worcestershire. The manor's origins stretch back to Anglo-Saxon times, and it undoubtedly fired Tolkien's imagination in his construction of the fictional world of Middle-earth.

However, it was perhaps more than just his childhood memories that Tolkien drew on in his creation of Bag End. "I came from the end of a bag, but no bag went over me", riddles Bilbo Baggins of Bag End in his contest of wits with the Dragon of Erebor. Just like the Hobbit, his creator was fascinated with puns, word games and riddles, and by literary sleights of hand. Furthermore, there are elements of social satire in the name of Bag End. As the eminent Tolkien scholar Tom Shipley has observed, Bag End is a literal translation of the French cul de sac, a term employed by snobbish British real estate agents in the early twentieth century who felt the English term "dead-end road" was just too vulgar.

Naturally, Tolkien's very English Baggins family would have no truck with this kind of Frenchified silliness, and so decided upon this suitably authentic local English name of Bag End.

As a rule, Tolkien despised the pretensions and snobbery that looked down on all things English. He preferred plain English in language, food and culture. Calling the Hobbit home of Bilbo Baggins "Bag End" is the epitome of everything that is honest, plain and thoroughly English. Through the Hobbits of Bag End, Tolkien both extols and gently parodies the Englishman's love of simple home comforts, seen as both delightful and absurd. Overall, the only thing that seems surprising is that he didn't write a parody aphorism along the lines of "The Hobbit's hole is his castle".

THE HOBBIT HOLE IS HIS CASTLE DAVID DAY

Brandy Hall was the residence of the Master of Buckland and the Brandybuck family on Buck Hill on the west bank of the Brandywine River. In later years it contained a vast library of books, including *Herblore of the Shire*, written by Meriadoc Brandybuck. It had three massive front doors, twenty lesser doors and a hundred round windows. But even the grandest of Hobbit mansions were so aligned with nature that they so blended into the contours of the landscape, that bigger and grander folk could pass through much of the Shire without being aware of those structures, or its inhabitants. And for the most part Hobbits liked it like that. For as those powerful kings and tyrants who built great castles and fortresses learned at their cost, pride comes before a fall. And time and again, upon Middle-earth, humble Hobbit holes proved to be the safest of sanctuaries.

Hobbits are the Spiritus Mundi of the English Shires. They were intended by Tolkien to be the Anglo-Saxon earth spirits who were most in touch with "the green and pleasant land" that was rural England. They lived in the bosom of the earth, and in so many ways were meant to define the essential virtues of the land and its people.

BRANDY HALL
LIDIA POSTMA

BATTLES
WARS AND
WARRIORS

ISILDUR AT THE GLADDEN FIELDS
MAURO MAZZARA

BATTLES

Tolkien's tales of Middle-earth abound in battles – from skirmishes and frays to cataclysmic conflicts of end-of-days proportions – and many have parallels with historic real-world battles as well as with those found in mythology and literature. The Battle of Dagorlad is comparable, in the utter destruction it wreaks and its massive body count, to the Battle of the Somme that Tolkien witnessed in 1916 during World War I.

The Battle of the Field of Celebrant (between the invading Balchoth and the Men of Gondor and the Éothéod) has similarities to the Battle of Catalaunian Fields in which the Romans and the Visigoth cavalry allied against the Huns of Attila in AD 451. The Great Battle in the War of Wrath at the end of the First Age was, as Tolkien acknowledged, primarily inspired by the Norse myth of the final battle-to-be, known as Ragnarök. The Battle of Pelennor Fields, in *The Lord of the Rings*, is certainly the most spectacular and richly observed of all Tolkien's battles and consequently has multiple parallels in, and allusions to, history, myth and literature.

DRAWING BLOOD   DAVID DAY

Forty years ago, John Blanche and Ian Miller were commissioned as the two star illustrators to create full-colour double-page spreads of Tolkien's battles in *A Tolkien Bestiary*. Both, of course, went on to distinguished careers where their ability to visualize bloody battles with much maiming, carnage and slaughter proved to be a profitable asset in the then relatively new media of video games workshops, role-playing publications and fantasy magazines and films. *The Fall of Gondolin*, as described in *The Silmarillion*, is classic John Blanche at full throttle. It is a scene filled with legions of evil Orcs, fire-breathing Dragons and demonic Balrogs. Blanche is equally impressive in his execution of *The Destruction of Angband*, *The Downfall of Númenor* and in that complex and climactic battle in *The Hobbit: The Battle of the Five Armies*.

In *The Battles of Tolkien*, the choice of the flamboyant artist Mauro Mazzara as the signature illustrator for the book, and subsequent books, was a bold one. Mauro produced over fifty remarkable works of art, and thirty of these are dramatic battles, duels or wars that range from the Creation of the World, the Wars of the Ainur, to the end of the Third Age with the Battle of the Black Gate. With many of these it is often interesting to compare and contrast his vision and style with that of other earlier illustrators' vision of similar events, such as his eagle-eye view of the Battle of the Five Armies. Mauro's aerial Great Eagle perspective of this battle and its swarming hordes before the gates of the Dwarf Kingdom-under-Mountain in *The Hobbit* is fascinating when compared to the Orc infantry-level view of the same battle created some 37 years later by our veteran battle-tried artist, John Blanche.

MAPPING TOLKIEN   JAMIE WHYTE

Maps were essential to the creation of Tolkien's legendarium. He drew them not only as aids for the reader in his published works, in forms which were extended and perfected by his son Christopher, but as aides to composition and conception in his private notes, in forms he never meant to be published. I discovered when researching the maps and plans I've made around Tolkien's work that if you know his maps, then reading the stories feels completely different. You can track the narrator's eye as it roves over the face of a spatially coherent geography.

The illustrated maps I've made, which are only intended to bring a little extra enhancement to a reader's experience, are not just informed by an interest in map making. My own interest in language and philology can't hold a candle to Tolkien's deep knowledge and expertise, but it's led me to see language as a kind of treasure hoard. The way Tolkien uses and crafts words, burnishing and regifting them from the deep past of our own language, reinforces this view: and the way his stories are presented alongside maps which are intrinsic to understanding them makes each volume seem like a treasure hoard in itself. Maps lead you to treasure, and maps are themselves treasure. I think Tolkien understood that.

THE BATTLE OF THE PELENNOR FIELDS
JAMIE WHYTE

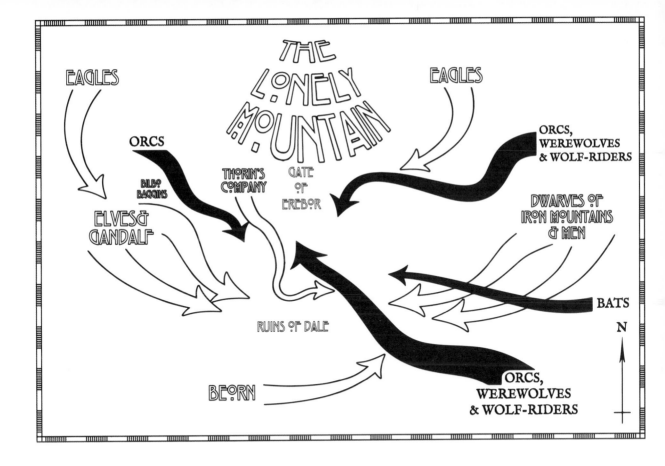

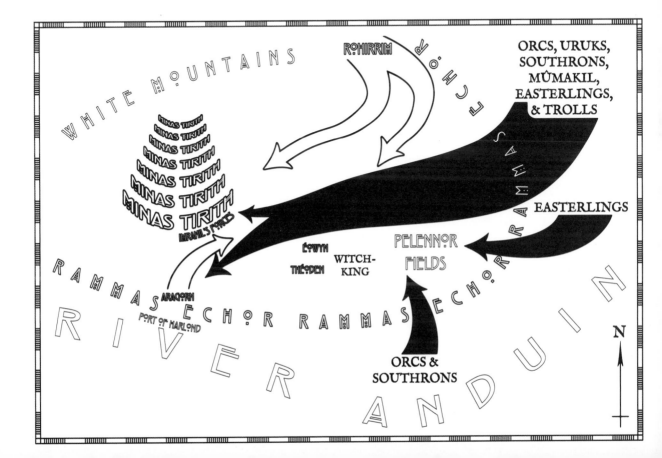

INVENT FOR THE SAKE OF IT
JOHN BLANCHE

Tolkien seems to have followed my career and certainly influenced my art. I discovered Tolkien at art school in the late sixties. I'd always been interested in mythology and history – the Dark Ages, Saxons, Vikings always appealed to me.

I had collections of toy soldiers and spent hours creating drawings inspired by them: battle scenes and pictures of ancient warriors on old rolls of wallpaper. And then I found Tolkien.

His weaving together of Norse mythology, history, and his own invention of the history and mythology of Middle-earth – the sheer imagination of it, all in a gripping narrative – got me hooked. Back then, fantasy art was frowned on at art school and wasn't seen as art. I was told never to invent for the sake of it and that I would never get a job painting pictures of angels, dragons, goblins and trolls. I was supposed to do something else, be something else.

But Tolkien had given me justification – and permission, if you like – to create fantasy works. To invent and imagine and create, for the sake of it. My final-year project was producing illustrations and graphic layouts for *The Hobbit*, and then, a decade later, I was invited to contribute some illustrations to *A Tolkien Bestiary*.

THE FALL OF GONDOLIN
JOHN BLANCHE

Around that time I'd started collecting metal miniatures, and some of the early fantasy miniatures that were just becoming available. I got involved with Citadel, a division of Games Workshop and produced the covers of *White Dwarf* (Games Workshop's gaming magazine) and the first edition cover of *Dungeons and Dragons*, as well as interior artwork for the magazines. In 1980 I joined Citadel as an illustrator and model soldier designer. In those early years I worked on a licensed range of *The Lord of the Rings* miniatures – there were about 85 sets produced throughout the 1980s.

In 1986 I was made Art Director at Games Workshop, and much later was one of a small team who flew out to pitch for the rights to produce a new *The Lord of the Rings* game and range of miniatures from New Line Cinema for the launch of the film trilogy. That series is still going today.

I'm semi-retired now but still attend Games Workshop conventions and people still bring me copies of old magazines to sign. Gelding (the farmhouse where Tolkien penned the first draft of *The Voyage of Éarendel the Evening Star*) is just up the road from me now. Tolkien has been on my path all these years. And it seems I got a few jobs painting pictures of angels, dragons, goblins and trolls after all.

THE DESTRUCTION OF ANGBAND
JOHN BLANCHE

BATTLE OF DAGORLAD

Dagorlad was the site, on the vast open plain in southeastern Rhovanion, near Mordor, of the greatest battle of Tolkien's Second Age wherein "All living things were divided in that day, and some of every kind, even of beasts and birds." Tolkien's Battle of Dagorlad (3434 SA) is the single greatest battle in the War of the Last Alliance, fought between the forces of Gil-galad, Elendil, Anárion and Isildur on the one hand and the Orc army of Sauron on the other.

ELENDIL, ANÁRION AND ISILDUR
VICTOR AMBRUS

↑ DEAD MARSHES
↑ MICHAEL FOREMAN

DEAD MARSHES
IAN MILLER

THE DEAD MARSHES AND THE SOMME

Perhaps more than any other battle in the history of Middle-earth the Battle of Dagorlad was informed by the author's own experience in the First World War and, specifically, as a soldier in the disastrous, semi-suicidal Battle of the Somme (1 July to 18 November 1916).

In that terrible conflict, Tolkien witnessed the near-total obliteration of the French landscape whose fields and woods were transformed into a blood-soaked wasteland littered with rotting corpses. It was a futile battle in which the armies fought for months, resulting in over a million casualties. There are powerful reminiscences of this in Tolkien's Battle of Dagorlad, which sees the greatest assemblage of combatants since the War of Wrath in the First Age, and which results in over a million casualties. The area, through which Frodo and Samwise pass in *The Lord of the Rings*, subsequently becomes a contaminated bogland where, even many centuries later, the faces of the slain can still be seen in the vile waters.

DEAD MEN OF DUNHARROW
VICTOR AMBRUS

OATHBREAKERS AND DEAD MEN

The Dead Men of Dunharrow are wraiths of pre-Númenórean Men of the White Mountains who haunt the Paths of the Dead. These legions of ghostly warriors are the spirits of Men who swore allegiance to Isildur, king of the Dúnedain, at the time of the Alliance of Elves and Men, but who broke that oath and betrayed him to Sauron. Thereafter all the warriors of the Men of the White Mountains were cursed and known as the Oathbreakers: tormented terrible wraiths that haunted the labyrinthine mountain paths of Dwimorberg.

Tolkien's Oathbreakers were in good part inspired by the many Norse and Germanic myths and real-life histories relating to broken oaths of fealty between warrior and lord, or oaths of alliance between king and king. For the peoples of northern Europe (as elsewhere), such oaths were legally binding. Oaths sworn upon weapons or oath rings were considered sacred trusts, and violation of those oaths had both real world and spiritual consequences. There was a belief that false oaths – sworn upon a sword – animated that sword, which became like an avenging entity that thirsted for blood and could be appeased only by the offender falling upon it. In Norse and German society, murder and manslaughter were not considered illegal offenses so long as they were carried out "honestly" and in the open, with the opponent given fair warning and the ability to defend himself. However, oath breaking was the most heinous of crimes, as it threatened the entire social order and hierarchy. This was especially true if the oath was broken for cowardly reasons, such as refusing the call to arms in the midst of battle, as was the case of the Men of White Mountains.

In the real-world honour code of these warrior societies, once an oath was broken, the offender would be banished and become an outlaw cast out of society. As an outlaw, he was beyond any lord or king's protection. He could be hunted down and, if caught, could legally be hanged: the most shameful of deaths that made entry into the afterworld Valhalla impossible. Like the Dead Men of Dunharrow, in Norse and Icelandic myths and sagas, oathbreakers are frequently trapped in a terrible limbo world, at least until some means of restitution might be discovered.

In Tolkien's tale, the curse is only lifted from the Oathbreakers after more than three millennia, when Isildur's Heir appears at last in the Paths of the Dead. Aragorn, son of Arathorn – the rightful heir and king of the Dúnedain – summons the Dead to fulfill the oath they broke long ago. This Shadow Host manifests itself in a mighty battalion of ghostly warriors that, at Aragorn's command, drive the Corsairs of Umbar from their fleet. Thus the souls of the Sleepless Dead are at last redeemed as the great pale army fade like a mist into the wind.

THE REFUGE OF DUNHARROW
GRAHAM BENCE

TÚRIN FACES GLAURUNG
KIP RASMUSSEN

→——◄

CONFLICTS   KIP RASMUSSEN

Tolkien's conflicts are irresistible. Illustrators have been compelled to depict Eowyn battling the Lord of the Nazgûl, Fingolfin vs. Morgoth, Glorfindel against the Balrog, almost as a rite of passage. But there are countless other struggles of equal importance, most of which involve a hero standing against a more powerful opponent. These include Feanor, Túrin, Lúthien and Ecthelion. These scenes call to us as illustrators.

TÚRIN TURAMBAR

One of the greatest of Edain heroes of the First Age. In good part, Tolkien's tale of Túrin and his father, Húrin, was inspired by Sigurd the dragon-slayer and his father, Sigmund, the heroes of the *Völsunga Saga*, the Norse epic described by the designer and poet William Morris (1834–96) as "the great story of the North, which should be to all our race what the tale of Troy was to the Greeks."

Tolkien's tale and the Norse saga begin with the deeds of the fathers. Both Húrin and Sigmund survive the near-extermination of their dynastic houses. In the Dagor Nírnaeth Arnoediad (Battle of Unnumbered Tears), Húrin is the last man standing in the Edain rearguard and, by single-handedly slaying 70 trolls, saves the retreating Noldor army from certain annihilation. With equal courage, Sigmund slaughters scores of his foes in acts of bloody revenge for the murder of his entire clan, including his eight brothers. However, both are eventually defeated: Húrin when his war axe withers in the heat of battle and Sigmund when his dynastic sword breaks in one last fatal duel.

Among the Elves and Men of Beleriand, Húrin the Steadfast is celebrated as "the mightiest warrior of mortal men" but, like the Norse hero Sigmund, he became even more renowned as the father of a dragon-slayer. Húrin's famous son is Túrin Turambar, the slayer of Glaurung, the Father of Dragons, while Sigmund's son is Sigurd the slayer of Fáfnir, the Prince of All Dragons.

Both dragon-slayers lay claim to broken dynastic swords that are re-forged: Túrin's sword is given the name Gurthang, meaning "iron of death", while Sigurd's is Gram, meaning "wrath". But, even so armed, neither of these heroes believe that these great worms could be slain by strength of arms alone. Courage and cunning are also required to defeat this terror. Túrin chooses to hide himself in a deep ravine at a river crossing, and when Glaurung attempts to cross over the gap, he drives his sword upward and into the massive monster's underbelly. Sigurd hides himself in a covered trench dug into the narrow road the beast takes each day to drink from a forest pool. When Fáfnir's great body passes over the trench the Völsung hero drives his sword Gram up into the dragon's exposed belly.

ANCALAGON DEPARTING FOR THE WAR OF WRATH
KIP RASMUSSEN

THE GREAT BATTLE

In the War of Wrath the great final battle between the forces of Morgoth the Dark Enemy and the Valarian Host of the West that brings an end to the First Age. While the Valar and Elves are ultimately victorious, the near-cosmic violence of the battle results in the shattering of the Iron Mountains and the sinking of almost all of the land of Beleriand.

Tolkien freely acknowledged that the Great Battle "owes, I suppose, more to the Norse vision of Ragnarök than to anything else." Certainly, there are a great number of similarities in these doomsday battles. Just as the final battle of Ragnarök will begin with the sounding of the Horn of Heimdall the Watchman of the Gods, Tolkien's Great Battle of the War of Wrath begins with the blast of the Horn of Eönwë, the Herald of the Valar. Gothmog, Lord of Balrogs, bears a flaming sword into the Great Battle, as does Surt, Lord of the Fire Giants, in the Norse legend. And in both battles, all the legions of good and evil – all creatures, spirits, demons and dragons – meet in one final terrible conflict.

Another likely source of inspiration, though less widely acknowledged, is to be found in the biblical Armageddon, a prophetic vision of the great battle fought between the forces of good and evil at the "end of time" as revealed in the Book of Revelation. There, in the duel between the Archangel Michael and the "Red Dragon", we find one possible source for the climatic duel between Eärendil the Mariner and Ancalagon the Black Dragon:

"Then war broke out in heaven. Michael and his angels fought against the dragon, and the dragon and his angels fought back. But he was not strong enough, and they lost their place in heaven. The great dragon was hurled down – that ancient serpent called the devil, or Satan, who leads the whole world astray. He was hurled to the earth, and his angels with him."

Just as the Red Dragon's downfall marks Satan's defeat, so Ancalagon the Black Dragon's downfall marks the defeat of Morgoth in Middle-earth. The Host of the West, like the Host of Heaven, prevails, and Morgoth the Dark Enemy is cast forever after into the darkness of the Eternal Void.

DRAGONS AND DRAGON-SLAYERS
DAVID DAY

Kip Rasmussen's love and dedicated study of the epic legends and tales of *The Silmarillion* has resulted in some of the most memorable illustrations of the Wars of Beleriand in the First Age. This has proved to be particularly true of those legendary battles and duels wherein Dragons play a dominant role. We certainly see this is in the duel between the dragon-slayer Túrin Turambar and the nightmare that was Glaurung, the Father of Dragons. Perhaps the most breath-taking single work is his magnificent *Ancalagon Departing for the War of Wrath* – the greatest winged fire drake of any age – commanding his legions of Dragons to enter the fray in the battle that finally results in the cataclysmic downfall of the forces of Morgoth, the Dark Enemy of the World, at the end of the First Age of Sun.

RIDERS OF ROHAN
VICTOR AMBRUS

ILLUSTRIOUS CAVALRYMEN DAVID DAY

Victor Ambrus created over twenty original and elegant line drawings of a dozen different tribes or races of Tolkien's Elves for *A Tolkien Bestiary* in 1979. Then, in 2002, Victor was once again tracked down to create new images: for *The World of Tolkien*, and this time in colour.

Once again, drawing on his immense and detailed knowledge of historical periods – particularly those related to military history – Victor was commissioned to portray the Riders of Rohan. It was believed that no one was more capable of portraying cavalrymen at full gallop than Victor Ambrus. Based on ancient Roman accounts of Gothic and Lombard cavalry charges, Victor conceived his first illustration of Eorl the Young, the First King of Rohan with his Éothéod Cavalry charging into the Battle of Celebrant. Then, shortly after, illustrated a second cavalry charge that in Tolkien's chronology occurred centuries later by Eorl's direct descendant: the 17th King of Rohan, Theoden in the famous *Ride of the Rohirim* that in *The Lord of the Rings* triggered the heroic and decisive Battle of the Pelennor Fields.

BALCHOTH

A barbarian horde of Easterlings from Rhovanion which, in 2510 TA, invade Gondor and engage with the Gondorian forces in the critical Battle of the Field of Celebrant. The tide of battle turns against the Balchoth when, unexpectedly, the cavalry of the Éothéod (ancestors of the Horsemen of Rohan) join forces with the Men of Gondor.

This has an historic precedent in the Battle of the Catalaunian Fields in AD 451 when the Roman army formed an alliance with the Visigoths (West Goths) and Lombard cavalry and defeated the barbarian horde of Attila the Hun. This is considered one of the most critical battles in the history of Europe as it turned back what seemed an unstoppable wave of Asiatic conquest of the West. In Middle-earth, in the wake of the Battle of the Field of Celebrant, the Balchoth confederacies rapidly disintegrated, as did the Hunnish confederacies after the Battle of Catalaunian Fields.

CIRION IN BATTLE WITH THE BALCHOTH
ANDREA PIPARO

THE FANTASY GENRE
ANDREA PIPARO

I consider myself a fantasy artist, although as an illustrator I am open to any theme. However my passion, and the majority of the projects which I have had the opportunity to work on, are mainly oriented towards the fantasy genre.

My creative process, and the desire to create illustrations that have a certain realism, often leads me in the preliminary stages of the work, to search for photographic material which can help me achieve greater closeness to reality in my representations. So in some ways I can say that I draw inspiration from life; the world and the wonder that surrounds us – something that isn't always considered.

The fantasy genre is, for me, a means to express the freedom of creativity and imagination. When I design or paint for personal projects – without the constraint of someone else's description – I have the opportunity to express myself with full creative freedom by drawing on my varied inner world. This is one of the aspects that I love most about my work: the freedom that fantasy, by definition, grants and the challenge to my personal interpretation.

BATTLE OF THE FIVE ARMIES

This climactic battle in J R R Tolkien's *The Hobbit* was fought over the treasure of the Lonely Mountain after the slaying of its guardian, Smaug the Golden Dragon. As Tolkien readily acknowledged, the basic plot of *The Hobbit* – complete with Dragon and treasure horde – was largely informed and inspired by his life-long study of the Anglo-Saxon epic poem *Beowulf*.

The huge Northman Beorn, Chieftain of the Beornings, Tolkien's fairy-tale version of the bear-cult hero of the real-life berserker warrior cult of the Germanic and Norse peoples, and Tolkien's Dwarves, resembling the warriors of Norse myth in their fighting style, would have been overrun had it not been for the sudden arrival of an unexpected ally.

The Eagles of Middle-earth are generally not prominent players in Tolkien's narratives, but their intervention is nearly always crucial – as in the Battle of the Five Armies – and they arrive at times of desperate need, frequently when rescue can be achieved only by the power of flight. They are part of a tradition of eagle-emissaries in myth, leading from the birds of the Greek god Zeus (the Roman Jupiter) to the vassals of Manwë, the Lord of the Winds of Arda.

BATTLE OF THE FIVE ARMIES
MAURO MAZZARA

SVINFYLKING

Also "swine array", *Svinfylking* was a wedge-shaped shield-wall formation employed by the Vikings as a shock troop tactic by infantry carrying heavy armaments. This was the formation and tactic Tolkien had Thorin Oakenshield employ at a pivotal moment in the Battle of the Five Armies in *The Hobbit*.

Here Tolkien was borrowing from real-world military history, as shield walls were an effective infantry strategy in warfare for thousands of years. The *Svinfylking* was a high-risk tactic used by Norsemen to break though enemy lines and create panic among the closed ranks of an army with superior numbers. It could be extremely effective, but it entirely depended on the initial monumental shock. If this flying wedge did not immediately break through enemy lines, the formation would soon collapse. Like many shield-wall tactics, it could often be outflanked and entirely encircled. And, indeed, this would likely have been the fate of Thorin Oakenshield and his warriors had it not been for the sudden unexpected appearance of Beorn the berserker skinchanger in the form of a gigantic black bear.

BATTLE OF
THE
FIVE ARMIES
JOHN BLANCHE

BEORNINGS AND HAVING FUN
MAURO MAZZARA

Animals are the subject I enjoy drawing the most. Imagine the fun I had drawing the Beornings, with that huge raging bear, or the Oliphaunts that are basically elephants as they could have been drawn in the Middle Ages. I felt a bit like the artist Dürer with his illustration of the rhino! Artists, in the Middle Ages and Renaissance, drew animals that were often based only on other artists' previous drawings, or simply oral descriptions of them. Just as with the game "broken telephone", the initial word often gets terribly distorted. With Oliphaunts, giant spiders, werewolves, I just "played" with animals; mixing and shaking them up, trying to get a tasty cocktail.

BERSERKERS

In their "holy battle rage", the historical berserkers felt themselves to be possessed by the spirits of enraged bears. As Odin's holy warriors, wearing only bearskins, they sometimes charged into battle unarmed, but in such a rage that they tore the enemy limb from limb with their bare hands and teeth. Such states, however, were essentially in imitation of what was the core miracle of the bear cult: the incarnate transformation of man into bear.

Once again, Tolkien uses a name to inspire his imagination. Beorn's name in Norse means "bear", and in *The Hobbit* we soon discover that Beorn is a "skin-changer" with the power of transformation from man to beast and beast to man. It is a supernatural power that eventually makes Beorn a critical factor in the outcome of the Battle of the Five Armies.

BEORNINGS
MAURO MAZZARA

THORIN OAKENSHIELD

IAN MILLER

THANGAIL

Sindarin word for "shield fence" and a defensive military formation consisting of a double rank of heavily armed knights used in situations when soldiers are heavily outnumbered in close-up hand-to-hand combat.

Here Tolkien was drawing on real-world military history, as shield walls have been used as an infantry strategy in warfare for thousands of years. However, the major weakness of the conventional shield wall is that it can be outflanked. This is the case in the wedge-shaped shield wall tactic used by Thorin Oakenshield at the Battle of the Five Armies (a tactic known to Norse warriors as the *Svinfylking*, or "swine array"). Tolkien's thangail attempts to address this problem in that it is flexible enough to curve around on itself and form an unbroken circle of shields and spears, thus countering any attempt by the enemy to outflank the defenders. Roman legions had a somewhat similar closed-rank defensive formation known as the testudo (or "tortoise") formation, akin to a turtle shell of shields on all sides and above.

THORIN

Thorin Oakenshield, son of Thráin, son of Thrór, was Dwarf King in the Blue Mountains in exile. Tolkien chose his name, Thorin, from the list of Dwarf names found in the twelfth-century Dvergatal or "Dwarf's Roll", in the Prose Edda. Appropriately enough for this daring and enterprising Dwarf it means "bold". However, Tolkien also gave him yet another Dwarf name drawn from the Dwarf's Roll, Eikinskjaldi, meaning "he of the Oakenshield". This was a name Tolkien viewed as a kind of riddle, and provoked the author into inventing a complex piece of background history for his Dwarf hero of *The Hobbit*. Tolkien explains that, during a battle in the Goblin Wars, Thorin broke his sword but fought on by picking up an oak bough, which he used as both a club and a shield.

A WOOD MARCHING ON A HILL

Beyond Ent being an Anglo-Saxon name for "giant", the inspiration for Tolkien's March of the Ents on Isengard came about in a rather negative way: through his dislike and, indeed, disapproval of William Shakespeare's treatment of myths and legends. His greatest abuse was heaped on one of the playwright's most popular plays, *Macbeth*.

The creation of the Ents, Tolkien explained, "is due, I think, to my bitter disappointment and disgust from schooldays with the shabby use made in Shakespeare of the coming of 'Great Birnam wood to high Dunsinane hill': I longed to devise a setting in which the trees might really march to war." Tolkien felt Shakespeare had trivialized and misinterpreted an authentic myth, providing a cheap, simplistic interpretation of the prophecy of this march of the wood upon the hill.

So in *The Lord of the Rings* Tolkien did indeed devise such a setting. And certainly, in his own March of the Ents, the fundamental opposition between the spirits of the forest and of the mountain was revealed and portrayed in a way that lends power and dignity to the archetypal miracle of a wood marching on a hill.

ENTS   IAN MILLER

When considering how best to portray the attacking Ents, I recalled a day I once spent in the Redwoods and chanced upon a fallen redwood tree. What impressed me the most I think – bulk notwithstanding – was the steel hawser tension of the exposed parts of the broken innards of the tree.

With this in mind – and the idea of Ents having the power in their hands to rip down stone walls – my assault on Isengard illustration gave the attacking Ents arms that looked very similar to interwoven steel cables.

On reflection, I think this was more than appropriate.

ENT ATTACK ON ISENGARD

IAN MILLER

HELM'S DEEP

IAN MILLER

The spread depicting the gathering of the dark forces before the wall in Helm's Deep was one of the most engaging images I created for *A Tolkien Bestiary* in my opinion, or at least one I really enjoyed creating. Whilst fortress cities and the mountain strongholds of the Dwarves feature in abundance, I think the drama that unfolded around Helm's Deep was one of the most engaging and visual sections of the book for me. Whenever I chance to watch a storm-driven sea crashing against a local breakwater I always think of the assault on the walls of Helm's Deep, silly perhaps, but there you are.

That said, when I saw castles in the sky at the National Gallery, red castles as I recall, with angels hanging out of them, I knew I was safe.

As to Ents, the sheer wonder of trees uprooting themselves en masse and then assaulting the fortified walls of Isengard, only to tear them down stone by stone is by any measure startling.

Add the Orcs, Uruk-hai, Dunlendings and Half-Orcs, not discounting Saruman himself to the pot, and you have an even more heady mix. Superb visuals and story line to boot. David's erudite narrative mapped the way, every time.

HELM'S DEEP

IAN MILLER

BATTLE OF THE PELENNOR FIELDS
VICTOR AMBRUS

STEEL ENGRAVING DAVID DAY

From the beginning, Ian Miller's distinctive, brooding drawings of Dragons, Dwarves and Orcs captured the popular imagination and resulted in them becoming firm fixtures and essential elements in the library of my books on Tolkien.

The magnificent, evil intelligence of his Dragons, the stubborn fierceness of his Dwarves and the twisted malignancy of his Orcs somehow conveyed – in a graphic style – a surface to his figures akin to that achieved through the technique of a fine steel-engraving. It is a unique and distinctive style that manages to visually link and bind all of these books together. All these elements and qualities found in his black and white line drawings came together – and were enhanced – in three magnificent full-colour spreads portraying the most vividly described battles in *The Lord of the Rings*: the Battle of Helm's Deep, the Ents March on Isengard and the Battle of Pelennor Fields. Ian's *Helm's Deep* in particular proved to be highly popular the week *A Tolkien Bestiary* was published. This was in good part because it appeared as an impressive full-colour spread in the *Sunday Observer* when – due to a national paper strike – it was the only broadsheet newspaper to appear in Britain on that weekend.

BATTLE OF THE PELENNOR FIELDS

The site, beneath the walls of Minas Tirith, of the most richly described conflict in the annals of Middle-earth, and the most dramatic (if not the final) battle of the War of the Ring. It took place on 15 March 3019 TA.

In his unfolding of the battle, Tolkien draws on many aspects of real-world military history, ranging over some 1,500 years of European warfare. To begin with, many of Gondor's opponents in the battle seem to have inspirations in the enemies of ancient Rome or Byzantium:

The Mûmakil (Oliphaunts) are tamed and mounted by Haradrim. These creatures evoke the elephants ridden by Carthaginians at the Battle of Zama, fought between the forces of Hannibal and the Roman troops led by Scipio, in 202 BC. The fierce Variags of Khand appear to have been inspired by the Varangians of Rus' who, in the ninth to eleventh century, launched a series of attacks on Byzantium. The Easterlings of Rhûn are likely inspired by the twelfth- and thirteenth-century Seljuk Turks of the Sultanate of Rûm in Anatolia, who harried and seized key Byzantine ports and other territories.

On the Gondorians' own side we have the Rohirrim, whose cavalry charge is solidly based on a historical Gothic cavalry action in support of the Romans at the Battle of Châlons in AD 451. When all seems lost for Gondor, the tide is turned by the appearance of the black-sailed ships of the Corsairs, carrying reinforcements from Gondor's coastal settlements, under the command of Aragorn.

MÛMAKIL

Mûmakil (or Mûmak) were the massive elephant-like animals used in battle by the Haradrim, known to the Hobbits as Oliphaunts. The Mûmakil were in large part inspired by historic accounts of use of war elephants in the Punic Wars (264–146 BC) between Rome and Carthage. The specific employment of Mûmakil by the Southrons in the Battle of Pelennor Fields may have been inspired by accounts of the historic Battle of Zama in 202 BC when the Roman army led by Scipio Africanus defeated the Carthaginian army of Hannibal with its division of war elephants.

However, Tolkien's descriptions of the Mûmakil appear to have been rather larger and more formidable beasts than the elephants recruited by the Carthaginians. Tolkien was certainly influenced by the discovery of bones and paleolithic cave drawings of the extinct species of elephant first identified as mammoths by Georges Cuvier in 1796. Tolkien makes a clear reference to mammoths – or their less hairy cousins the mastodons – in one of his annotations: "The Mûmak of Harad was indeed a beast of vast bulk, and the like of him does not walk now in Middle-earth; his kin that live still in latter days are but memories of his girth and majesty."

ELEPHANTS AND HORSES   IAN MILLER

Somebody once suggested that Surrealism was nothing more than the unlikely juxtaposition of objects and ideas, but I'm not sure that helps me much here. When I discovered I could draw whole, rather than partial, elephants and camels I was elated, but sadly my horses still look like large Alsatian dogs.

HISTORY AND HORSES   MAURO MAZZARA

I deeply admire Tolkien for creating his own mythology. I can only imagine the kind of huge effort behind such a colossal work. I've always studied history with interest, as I believe it helps us to understand who or what we are in the present day. Too often people forget or ignore it and only see what world we live in now!

As an illustrator, my historical interest is somehow "forced", because I must know the type of armours, clothes and fashion. I must represent, for example, Rohan being of the Middle Age, Rivendell as a kind of Renaissance, Isengard a vision of the Iron Age, and so on.

History, the history of design, the history of weapons…everything matters if you're going to draw something "believable".

As a child, I remember myself drawing both fantastic and fantasy subjects as well as animals. My father has been correcting the anatomy of my horses since I was probably six years old. So I grew up drawing both from life and from the world I created myself, in the meanwhile.

BATTLE OF PELENNOR
IAN MILLER

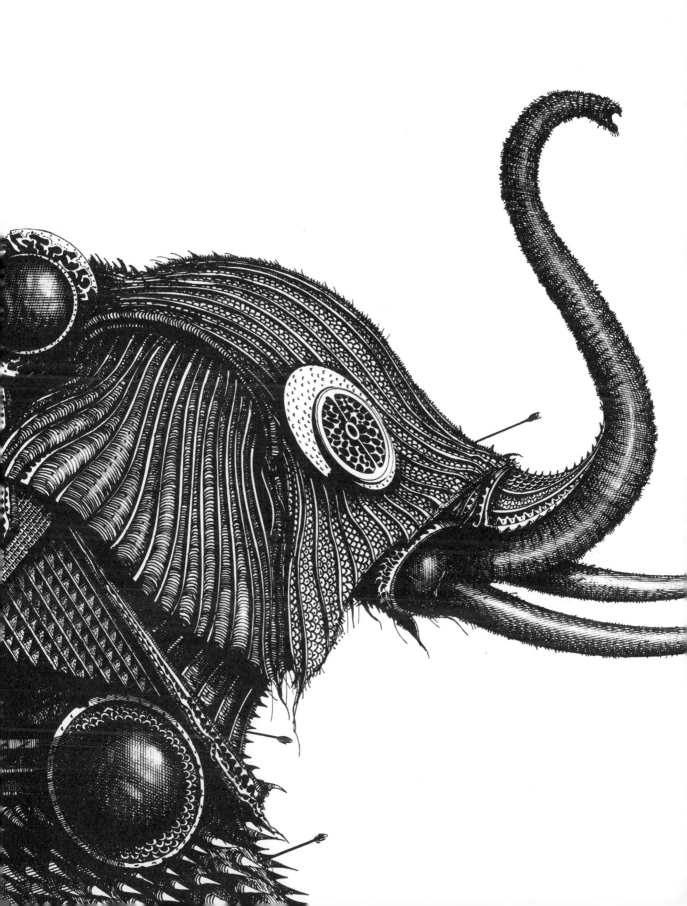

BATTLE AT THE BLACK GATE

In most of the world's mythologies, we find epic tales dealing with the cosmic battle between good and evil: the fate of the world is held in balance as the mass forces of evil threaten to overwhelm and obliterate the apparently doomed forces of good. In Tolkien's *The Lord of the Rings*, the climactic battle between good and evil is played out in the Battle of the Black Gate. In his epic novel, Tolkien combined the theme of the cosmic battle with another universal mythological motif, the "External Soul", known, in multiple forms, by "peoples from Hindoostan [sic] to the Hebrides", as James George Frazer observed in his famous *The Golden Bough: A Study of Comparative Religion* (1890). A warlock, giant or other supernatural being, Frazer explained, "is invulnerable and immortal because he keeps his soul hidden away in some secret place [or object]; this secret is revealed to the hero, who seeks out the warlock's soul, heart, life or death (as it is variously called), and by destroying it, simultaneously kills the warlock."

In *The Lord of the Rings*, the mighty Sauron, who commands vastly superior armies and terrible supernatural powers, appears to be an unstoppable force in the final cosmic Battle at the Black Gate. However, at that very moment when total victory seems within his grasp, Sauron discovers that he is supremely vulnerable and mortally threatened as Frodo the Hobbit slips the One Ring onto his finger: "The Dark Lord was suddenly aware of him, the Eye piercing all shadows looked across the plain…the magnitude of his folly was revealed to him in a blinding flash, and…he knew his deadly peril and the thread upon which his doom now hung." The One Ring that effectively contains Sauron's "external soul" is on the hand of the Hobbit who now threatens its destruction in the volcanic fires of the Cracks of Doom.

EMOTION   MAURO MAZZARA

In *Battle of the Black Gate*, as with *The Horde*, I wanted to give character to every subject at the very moment that Mount Doom explodes. Someone is falling in that moment, someone else understands, but most of them are still struggling to survive the battle. Every time I draw these scenes, I embody every subject I draw, imagining myself in their place, trying to give a wide range of emotions.

BATTLE OF THE BLACK GATE
MAURO MAZARRA

LINDA GARLAND

Linda Garland graduated from Wolverhampton College of Art and Design with a degree in Fine Art in the late 1960s. There she met her future husband Roger, and discovered they shared a love of Tolkien among other things. Linda's first commissions were illustrations for *A Tolkien Bestiary* in 1979 with Roger's own commissions from Tolkien's publishers following in 1981.

MELVYN GRANT

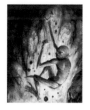

Melvyn "Mel" Grant is an artist and illustrator who, after a brief sojourn in Europe working as a guitarist and even designing and building some unusual electric guitars, returned to illustration work in various media, including animation. Grant has produced illustrations for many books, including the *Fighting Fantasy* gamebooks and is known for being one of the artists associated with Iron Maiden's mascot Eddie, and five of Iron Maiden's album covers.

SAM HADLEY

Sam Hadley graduated from Falmouth University and jumped right into a successful freelance illustration career. He has worked on a variety of projects in advertising, packaging and editorial and has created book covers, billboards, video game characters and everything in between for clients including Saatchi & Saatchi, Carlsberg, Madison Square Gardens and English National Opera.

DAVID KEARNEY

David Kearney is an illustrator and artist. David spent over 20 years with the illustration agency Artist Partners and in that time worked on a wide variety of publications for adults and children. He now spends his time painting landscapes and anything that interests him.

PAULINE MARTIN

Pauline Martin studied at Brighton Polytechnic in the 1970s and developed an unusual and unique style of watercolour painting. She illustrated the beautiful *Moonlight and Fairyland* by Laurence Housman in 1978 and the following year contributed several exquisite pieces to *A Tolkien Bestiary*.

MAURO MAZZARA

Mauro Mazzara started drawing at the age of two and hasn't stopped. Published in the Annual Illustrators of Children's Books in 2002, Mauro joined the Brera Art Academy to study painting. He works as a freelance illustrator in publishing, fashion and advertising and teaches drawing and painting at Scuola Internazionale Comics in Brescia.

IAN MILLER

Ian Miller graduated from the Painting Faculty of St Martin's School of Art in 1970 and went on to become an artist, illustrator and writer. His film work includes two Ralph Bashki films, and pre-production on *Shrek* in the 1990s. The first collection of his work, *The Green Dog Trumpet* was published in 1979 by Dragon's Dream. This was followed shortly afterwards by a second volume entitled *Secret Art* and then *Ratspike*, co-authored with John Blanche.

ANDREW MOCKETT

Andrew Mockett is an artist and printmaker specialising in woodcuts and multiple screen-printings and has produced printed textiles for Givenchy and Paul Smith. He is currently represented by the Rebecca Hossack Gallery, in Conway Street, London and Mott Street, New York, and his work has featured in the public collections of several galleries including London's Tate Modern and Victoria and Albert Museum.

TURNER MOHAN

(James) Turner Mohan is a self-taught fantasy artist and illustrator based in Long Island, New York. His love of (and fascination with) history and mythology informs his fantasy illustration and he describes his incredibly detailed works as "a kind of fictional anthropology". He works in pen and ink but has also started to explore watercolour and sculpture and has recently been apprentice to a period-recreation armour maker.

ANDREA PIPARO

Andrea Piparo graduated from the Art School of via Ripetta and continued his studies by attending the illustration course at the International School of Comics. He has exhibited his works in various collective exhibitions and at various events such as Fantastika, Dozza (Bologna) in 2014 and at Wow Comics Space (Milan) in 2015.

SUE PORTER

Sue Porter is a much loved children's book illustrator and author with more than 50 books to her name. Her earliest commissions were for *A Tolkien Bestiary* and the lavishly illustrated *World Tales* collection edited by Idries Shah in 1979. She is the author and illustrator of the *Parsnip* series for young children, and has contributed illustrations to several of Eva Ibbotson's stories.

LIDIA POSTMA

Lidia Postma trained as an illustrator at the Amsterdam Gerrit Rietveld Academie and went on to become an illustrator and author. Lidia was honoured with a Golden Brush award in 1976 for her illustrations for a Hans Christian Andersen collection, and the prestigious Golden Apple at the Biennale in Bratislava in 1979. In the 1980s Lidia widened the scope of her work as an illustrator and began to explore sculpture and reliefs.

KIP RASMUSSEN

Kip Rasmussen is an illustrator, author and independent film producer. Inspired by the works of J R R Tolkien, he interrupted his career as a family therapist to illustrate scenes from *The Silmarillion*, the work he considers more fundamental than both *The Hobbit* or *The Lord of the Rings*. His illustrations have been included in Peter Jackson's DVD "The Hobbit: The Desolation of Smaug". Kip is a published author as well as a producer of feature-length science-fiction and fantasy films.

DAVID ROBERTS

David Roberts began his career in fashion illustration before moving into children's book illustration. He has illustrated many books for children of all ages and is best known for his work with Julia Donaldson, Philip Ardagh and Chris Priestley. He has been nominated for the CILIP Kate Greenaway Medal, and in 2006 won the Nestlé Children's Book Prize Gold Award for his illustrations in *Mouse Noses on Toast*.

ŠÁRKA ŠKORPÍKOVÁ

Šárka Škorpíková is a Zoology student at Charles University in Prague but spends her free time painting and hopes to pursue a career in illustration and art stationery after finishing her course. She is a huge fan of Tolkien – *The Silmarillion* in particular – and draws on her love of wild landscapes when painting scenes from his works.

JAMIE WHYTE

Jamie Whyte is an artist and illustrator specialising in "creative cartography", which he defines as the creation of beautiful yet functional illustrated maps for print. As an illustrator and designer he has created artwork for fiction and non-fiction books, made logos for several companies and organisations and his work was recently featured in the three-part BBC4 history series *The Silk Road*.

VICTOR AMBRUS

Victor Ambrus FRSA is a writer and illustrator and an Associate of the Royal College of Art, a Fellow of both the Royal Society of Arts and the Royal Society of Painters, Etchers and Engravers, and was also a patron of the Association of Archaeological Illustrators and Surveyors. He has illustrated many books for children and is now known from his appearances on the television archaeology series *Time Team*.

GRAHAM BENCE

Graham Bence is a painter and illustrator specialising in landscapes painted in oils and acrylics. His work has featured in a number of books, including a jacket illustration for a first edition of Louis de Bernières *Captain Corelli's Mandolin*.

JOHN BLANCHE

John Blanche is an illustrator and modeller who is best known for his work with Games Workshop's *White Dwarf* magazine and Warhammer publications and models. He became the Art Director for Games Workshop in the 1980s and continues to attend conventions today.

JAROSLAV BRADAC

Jaroslav Bradac studied at the Academy of Arts, Architecture and Design in Prague in the 1960s and moved to London in 1969. He works in a range of media and across many disciplines including sculpture and collage and has illustrated several books for adults and children. He animated and directed the animated version of "The Treatise" in the film of *Steppenwolf* (1974).

ALLAN CURLESS

Allan Curless was a political cartoonist for 16 years, working mostly for the *Sunday Times*. His first children's book, *Cat's Song* with Andrew Matthews, was shortlisted for the Mother Goose Award and the Smarties Prize in 1994. He is perhaps best known for his chapter icon illustrations for Brian Jacques's *Redwall* series. He died in 1997.

SALLY DAVIES

Sally Davies is a painter and illustrator who uses collage, printing and layering techniques as well as a more traditional use of oils and acrylics to build her images. She has illustrated a number of books for adults and children.

JON DAVIS

Jon Davis is an illustrator, best known for his prolific career in comics including *Lady Penelope* and *TV Century 21*, and his illustrations for *Rupert the Bear* and Ladybird Books. He began his career in science fiction illustration after reading *The Hobbit* and *The Lord of the Rings*. He was awarded an MBE for services to Children's Literature in the Queen's New Year's Honours List in 2013 under his full name, John Frederick Charles Davis.

MICHAEL FOREMAN

Michael Foreman is one of the best-known and most prolific creators of children's books, with more than 250 books to his name. He won the 1982 and 1989 Kate Greenaway Medals for British children's book illustration and has been nominated twice for the Hans Christian Andersen Award for his contribution as a children's illustrator.